JESUS, SON OF DAVID

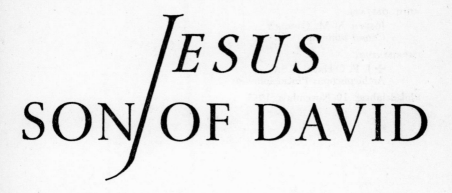

JESUS
SON OF DAVID

BY *Mother Mary Eleanor, S.H.C.J.*

#4716

ILLUSTRATED BY *George Pollard*

MILWAUKEE
The Bruce Publishing Company

NIHIL OBSTAT:

    Joseph A. M. Quigley
    Censor librorum

IMPRIMATUR:

    ✠ J. F. O'Hara, C.S.C.
    Archiepiscopus Philadelphiensis

Philadelphiae, 10 Novembris, 1953

Catholic University of America Classification:
Lynn, BQT806   Dewey, 232.9

Library of Congress Catalog Card Number: 55–7864

FOREWORD

Most of the words attributed to our Lord in this book were really said by him, except that the thee's and thou's have usually been changed to you's. A very few have been invented. The deeds are true, except for the little imagined ones in the hidden life in Egypt and Nazareth. People's thoughts have been invented, and what the neighbors said. There are, of course, many scenes in the life of Jesus which are not included. As St. John said, at the end of his Gospel, "If they were all written, every one, the world itself . . . would not be able to contain the books that should be written."

CONTENTS

	FOREWORD	V
I	MARY IS VISITED BY AN ANGEL	1
II	MARY VISITS HER COUSIN ELIZABETH	7
III	JESUS IS BORN IN BETHLEHEM	16
IV	JESUS VISITS HIS FATHER'S HOUSE	29
V	JESUS GOES DOWN INTO EGYPT	36
VI	JESUS IS LOST FOR THREE DAYS	42
VII	JESUS IS BAPTIZED BY JOHN	47
VIII	JESUS GOES TO A WEDDING	54
IX	NICODEMUS COMES TO JESUS BY NIGHT	61
X	JESUS IS DRIVEN OUT OF NAZARETH	68
XI	PETER, ANDREW, JAMES, AND JOHN BECOME FISHERS OF MEN	74
XII	SIMON THE PHARISEE GIVES A DINNER	81
XIII	THE MOTHER OF JESUS HELPS IN A HIDDEN WAY	88
XIV	JESUS FEEDS FIVE THOUSAND	94
XV	PETER IS GIVEN THE KEYS TO HEAVEN	102
XVI	JESUS PREACHES IN THE TEMPLE	110
XVII	JESUS RAISES LAZARUS FROM THE DEAD	117
XVIII	JESUS MAKES TWO STOPS IN JERICHO	126
XIX	MARY MAGDALEN BREAKS A JAR OF PERFUME	133
XX	JESUS ENTERS JERUSALEM LIKE A KING	139
XXI	JUDAS SELLS HIS MASTER FOR SILVER	146

XXII   JESUS GIVES HIS DISCIPLES THE BREAD OF LIFE   152

XXIII   JESUS PRAYS IN THE GARDEN OF GETHSEMANI   161

XXIV   PETER DENIES HIS LORD   167

XXV   JESUS IS CONDEMNED TO DEATH   173

XXVI   JESUS DIES ON THE CROSS   179

XXVII   JESUS IS LAID IN THE TOMB   186

XXVIII JESUS RISES ON THE THIRD DAY   192

XXIX   JESUS RETURNS TO THE UPPER ROOM   199

XXX   JESUS COMMISSIONS HIS DISCIPLES AS APOSTLES   207

XXXI   JESUS ASCENDS INTO HEAVEN AND SENDS IN HIS
        PLACE THE HOLY SPIRIT   214

        EPILOGUE: THE APOSTLE JOHN BEGINS TO WRITE
        HIS GOSPEL   221

JESUS, SON OF DAVID

.

Chapter I

MARY IS VISITED BY AN ANGEL

 ARY paused a moment to think. Had she forgotten anything? Dried fish — barley — salt — anise seed . . . No, not anything. She shifted her basket a little and started to pick her way through the jostling crowds in the market place.

"Dried figs, little lady? Goat cheese — honey — Take something home to your mother, my pretty!" Bony old fingers reached out to her, urging her to buy. Brown old faces wrinkled into smiles.

"Sh! Her mother's dead, and her father too. Don't you know who she is?"

"No, who is she?"

"She's the daughter of Joachim and Anne — the little girl who lived in the Temple. She's Mary."

"Ah, she's a pretty one! She has her mother's dark eyes and dear ways! She's a lovely one, the little lady!"

"Dried figs — goat cheese — honey . . . "

Mary smiled to herself as she moved past the crowded booths out into the street. It was spring in Nazareth. Potters and weavers and silversmiths were working in the open doorways of their shops. They called out to her as she passed.

1

"Nice water jars for sale. Step this way, little lady" . . .

"Bracelets for the little lady" . . .

She pulled her mantle closer about her and hurried past shyly. She was glad when she reached the well; that was more familiar territory. A group of girls loitered by it, their water jars beside them, talking and laughing.

"Come and join us, Mary," one of them called.

She smiled and shook her head. "No, not today, thank you." And she walked on past them.

"Who's that? I don't know her."

"That's Mary, the one who has just come back from Jerusalem to marry Joseph the carpenter."

"Joseph the carpenter? He's the best carpenter in Galilee — and the kindest. He'll make her a good husband."

Mary turned off into a narrow lane. Now that she was out of the crowd she slackened her pace. It was a day to make one want to sing. The sun was almost blinding as it shone on the white-walled houses, and the air was sweet with blossoms. She thought of a song she had learned in the Temple — a song of the poet-king David:

Sing ye to the Lord a new song
Because he hath done wonderful things. . . .

The lane led up to a narrow terrace, bordered with crooked olive trees. A row of small houses was built along it, up against the side of the hill. She pushed open the door of the last house, gave one more look around, and went in out of the sunshine.

The house was empty — she was glad of that. She was living with relatives, and they were very good to her. They treated her like their own daughter. But the noisy village life was a complete change from the life she had lived in the Temple. Neighbors were constantly coming and going. "Did you hear that Rachel is to marry Levi the wine merchant?" "Our little Jacob is sick. Could someone sit with him while we go to town?" "Our hen didn't lay today. Could you spare us an egg?" They came for things like these. It was Mary who fetched the egg, Mary who sat with little Jacob. He would soon be asleep in her lap, his hot little head pillowed on her arm! It was a friendly life, this life in Nazareth, but she could not help missing the Temple. And so today she was glad to be alone.

She closed the door behind her and set down her basket. Things were just as she had left them — the loaf of black bread, the cheese, the dried figs. She had put them there in case the children should come in hungry. She would leave them there for supper.

Was there anything she ought to do now? She had already fed the hens, filled the lamps, ground the barley for tomorrow's baking. No, there was nothing — not until time to get supper. She was free to do what she liked.

Behind the main room was a kind of storeroom, cut into the side of the hill. It was cavelike and quiet. She went in there and shut the door. The bare earth floor was very different from the wide paved court of the Temple, with its great bronze doors and silver lamps. That did not matter! She closed her eyes and prayed. A lizard crawled up the wall, looked at her with his bright eyes, and darted into a hole. Slowly the minutes passed, but she was not aware of them.

Suddenly she heard a movement and looked up. Someone was with her, someone shining and beautiful. That was strange! No one had opened the door! She was sure she was not dreaming. She shut her eyes and opened them again, but he was still there, more beautiful than ever. He could not be anyone earthly. Could he be an angel? Angels came sometimes to very holy persons — to men like Jacob or Elias. Could an angel be coming to her? She trembled to see him so near. After a moment he spoke.

Hail, full of grace, the Lord is with thee.
Blessed art thou among women. . . .

Yes, he was an angel — an angel from God, and he was calling her blessed, calling her full of grace! Now she was more startled than ever. She did not know it, but she was breathing very hard.

The angel looked at her lovingly. She was so young and good! He leaned toward her ever so slightly.

Fear not, Mary, for thou hast found grace with God. . . .

She was less startled now; she was breathing more easily. He could begin to tell her God's message.

Behold, thou shalt conceive in thy womb and shalt bring forth a Son, and thou shalt call his name Jesus. . . .

Mary turned pale as he spoke, but the angel went on with his message.

He shall be called great, and shall be called the Son of the Most High, and the Lord God will give him the throne of David his father, and he shall be king over the house of Jacob forever, and of his kingdom there shall be no end.

Mary knew what those words meant. Every Jewish girl knew. Those were the words men used when they spoke of the Redeemer, the Messias who was coming to save his people. Often she had heard the Scribes read the words of prophecy from the great scrolls of the Prophet Isaias. And often she had watched a faraway look come into the eyes of old Anna, the widow, as they sat over their weaving in the women's part of the temple. "Listen," Anna would say, stopping her loom as the words came through the latticed window. "Listen, my pretty one. He is to be called 'Wonderful, Counselor, God the Mighty' and 'Prince of Peace.'" Yes, Mary knew.

Most Jewish girls dreamed, too, of being his mother. Their mothers taught them to pray for it. And the old widow Anna, who was almost like a mother to Mary, there in the Temple, used to say to her sometimes: "Pray for it, Child! Pray for it to the dear Jehovah. It is what all women ask for." But to Mary, bending over her loom, this seemed too much to ask for. And so to the dear, mighty God, she had said a different prayer. She had asked to be the Redeemer's little handmaid, his little servant, to serve him and his mother all her days. She prayed for this in secret in the Temple. When the silver trumpets sounded for the Morning Sacrifice she prayed for it, and when the last light of day stole from the quiet court and she lay on her little bed. There in the great, still night she promised God never to belong to anyone but to him and his Prince of Peace. And so, when the rabbis sent her home to marry Joseph, she told him of her promise and her prayer. He understood.

And now here was an angel of the Most High God telling her that it was she whom God had chosen to be the mother of his Son! She was very puzzled, and she said to the angel:

How can this be? Because I know not man.

The angel had his answer ready. It was part of the message he had brought from God.

The Holy Spirit shall come upon thee, and the power of the Most High shall overshadow thee; and therefore the Holy One to be born shall be called the Son of God. And behold Elizabeth, thy kinswoman, also has conceived a son in her old age, and she who was called barren is now in her sixth month; for nothing is impossible to God.

He stepped back and waited; it was Mary's turn to speak now. She did not seem uncertain any longer, for she was full of grace. She even smiled a little as she answered:

Behold the handmaid of the Lord. Be it done unto me according to Thy word.

The angel bowed to her as though she were a queen. Then, quite suddenly, he was gone.

Mary stayed just as he had left her, alone with her secret — the mightiest in the world. Caesar did not know about it in his palace in Rome, nor King Herod in his courts in Jerusalem, nor the Chief Priest in the Temple. Only she knew it, and she would not tell, for it was God's secret, not hers. Jesus was coming, the hope of all the nations. Jesus was coming, and he was going to be her Son . . .

A moth brushed past her and she did not feel it. Shadows grew longer and she did not know. Then suddenly there were footsteps on the path. The outer door opened and there were voices. At first she hardly heard. Then gradually the sounds reached through to her mind. She stirred and roused herself like someone waking from sleep, trying to remember where she was. Oh yes, now she remembered! She went to the door as quickly as she could. It was time to be getting the supper.

Chapter II

MARY VISITS HER COUSIN ELIZABETH

SMALL caravan moved slowly up the steep road that wound up the ridge above Nazareth. There were three or four men on foot, as many women riding, and several dark-eyed children.

"Mary," the children were saying, "we're glad you're coming with us. Why are you going to Ain-Karim, Mary?"

Mary smiled down at them. "To visit my cousin Elizabeth."

"Is she young like you, Mary?"

"No, dear, she is old, and very, very kind."

"Children, don't you be bothering Mary," one of the women said. Mary protested, smiling, but the children were silent for a time, and she rode along, busy with her thoughts. It was less than a week since the angel's visit, but it seemed much longer, for the secret made everything different. Jesus had become a part of all her thoughts, whether she was grinding corn or baking bread or spinning flax. He was her little King now and ruled her mind.

The angel had not said anything about her visiting Elizabeth, but Elizabeth was old and she too had a secret. "I must go to her," Mary had thought, the night after the angel's visit, as she lay in bed. "I must go to her and help her." They could sit in

7

the warm spring sunshine, sewing and being glad together. After
the baby came there would be many things to do.

She had been fortunate that a caravan was leaving so soon for
the south. They were kind, friendly people, these neighbors who
had offered to escort her to Ain-Karim on their way to Jerusalem.
The children kept running to her and putting their soft, shy hands
in hers. Some day, Jesus will be doing that, she thought.

"Mary, tell us a story."

"What story?" she asked, smiling. But she was thinking: *He
shall be called the Son of the Most High. He shall be called
Wonderful, Counselor, God the Mighty, Prince of Peace.*

That first day, they rode through the rich green plains of
Esdraelon. Sometimes they rode in silence; sometimes they talked.
The women talked of babies teething and learning to walk. These
things too Jesus would be doing before very long! The men spoke
of crops and prices, of some new edict of Caesar, or of some further
outrage of Herod, who had killed two of his sons. Some said he
was plotting to kill a third. Mary tried not to hear these things,
but when the talk turned on the Messias, she listened.

"The Messias? Oh yes, he is coming. The rabbis say it may be
soon. We hope he will free us from Roman rule." A Pharisee whom
they met rubbed his hands and added, "We Pharisees are just
waiting for him to take over control. Then we'll have things all
our way." A bushy-haired merchant standing nearby only shrugged
his shoulders. "The Messias? That's only some Jewish notion. I'm
a Roman myself."

Mary smiled to herself and guarded her secret. The long ears of
her donkey bobbed up and down in front of her as she rode. The
hills of Samaria lay lovely on the horizon. Yes, the Messias was
coming very soon. She knew, but she did not tell.

The second day they rode through Samaria, but it was unfriendly
country, and they traveled cautiously, saying little. The third and
fourth days they passed between olive orchards in rocky, rugged
Judea. The trees clung to the hillsides with gnarled roots, but there
was hardly a hill that was not holy.

"This is Bethel," Mary said to the children, as it came into view around a bend in the road. "This is where Jacob saw the ladder reaching into heaven."

"Tell us about it," the children clamored. "Were there angels?"

"Yes, many angels, ascending and descending."

At last they reached the brow of a steep hill, and looking ahead, they saw the turrets and towers of Jerusalem shining in the sun. At the very top were the gold and white pinnacles of the Temple. The travelers were silent a moment as they looked. Then they started to descend and olive trees blocked their view. Shortly afterward, they turned off on the road to Ain-Karim, and they did not see the city again.

"Please tell us a story," the children begged. "Tell us about Rebecca at the well."

"Once there was a man named Isaac," Mary began. The sun was hot, but the children forgot to mind it. They could listen to her stories all day long. And so they rode the last four miles together. Suddenly as they rounded a curve, they saw the walled town of Ain-Karim, perched on the side of the hill.

"Mary," the children were saying, "tell us about the Temple. Tell us about the boy Samuel."

Mary smiled down at them, but her thoughts were far away. So this was Elizabeth's city! At last she was almost there!

"Please, Mary, just one more story!" The children pulled at her cloak with small brown hands, but one of the men signaled to the group to stop. He hailed a merchant coming toward them.

"Please, sir, can you tell us the way to Zachary's house? It is Zachary the priest we want."

The merchant pulled his donkey to a stop. "Zachary the priest? Oh, yes, he was the one who was struck dumb in the Temple while he was offering the incense. Go through the market place and past the Synagogue. Then take the first turn left. It's the third house."

"Did you hear what he said, Mary?"

Of course she heard! She was turning troubled eyes on the stranger. Zachary struck dumb? Zachary, the husband of Elizabeth, who was going to have a son? Had she come to share sorrow with them instead of joy?

"Good day to you," the merchant said, pulling the reins of his donkey, and he continued on his way.

"Mary, why do you look so sad?" the children asked. They stroked her slender hand with their hot little fingers. "We love your stories, Mary."

"Children, don't you be bothering Mary," one of the women said. "You say good-by to her and thank her for being so good to you. We're going to leave her now."

They looked suddenly shy and sad. Mary reached down into her saddlebag and brought out a handful of dates. "Here's something for you," she said to console them. She lifted the smallest one and kissed him. And so they parted, she and the little group. They had been good to bring her all this way when they were in a hurry to reach Jerusalem. "Thank you," she said. "May the Lord bless you."

She sat looking after them a moment as they turned and started back over the road they had come. Soon they were lost from sight in a cloud of dust, and she headed her donkey through the narrow gate into the busy traffic of the town. *Through the market place and past the Synagogue* . . . She would have to watch carefully where she was going, for the streets were narrow and crowded. Donkeys almost brushed the houses with their saddlebags when they passed each other, and people on foot had to step into doorways to get out of their way. Children were everywhere.

"Penny, lady, penny?" A small, grimy hand pulled at her sleeve. Looking down, she saw a ragged urchin whose sharp little ribs showed through his torn tunic. She reached into the bag at her waist and pulled out a coin, though there were not many in it. "Here," she said, and she handed it to him smiling. "The Lord bless you."

"Thank you, lady." He smiled back shyly. She was such a young, pretty lady! "Thank you."

She was picking her way through the market place now. Old women who were very like the old women in the Nazareth market were entreating her to buy: "Honey, my pretty one. Fresh honey from the comb. Take some home to your mother." They smiled at her their crooked, toothless smiles. Mary's throat tightened at the sight of them. They looked so very poor! But Jesus was coming, and he would be the friend of the poor.

She passed the Synagogue next and could hear the little boys droning away at their lessons in the Synagogue School, reciting verses from the Torah in their shrill, singsong way. Would Jesus learn like that, or would he know without learning — the little Son of God?

Take the first left turn. It's the third house. . . . Her thoughts reverted to Zachary struck dumb and Elizabeth waiting for her child. They would be patient, she knew. In a moment she would turn the corner; in a moment she would be standing on the doorstep, knocking at Zachary's door. Elizabeth would be very much surprised. . . .

*   *   *

Zachary sat under a lemon tree in his walled garden, thinking. He had much to think about these days. Life had been very different, yet very wonderful, since the day, six months before, when he had been struck dumb in the Temple offering the incense. He had waited all his life for it to fall his lot to offer the incense. At last the day had come, and it was really his turn to put on the linen vestments, go into the Holy Place, and burn the incense in the golden dish, just as the trumpets sounded and the priests and people waited, hushed. He had gone in, and then he had not come out. The people had waited and waited, while the Temple musicians grew restless in their places. The priests began to look about restlessly. Where was Zachary? Why did he not come out and pronounce the words of benediction? Finally he had come, but there was a strange look on his face. He had stood with his hands raised to say the words of blessing, but no words came. He had stood there white and trembling till someone stepped out from the line of waiting priests and led him out of the Temple. "He has

seen a vision," people whispered to each other. "Zachary has seen
a vision." But he could not speak to tell them what it was.

"We are having a son," he had written on his wax tablet for
Elizabeth when he reached his home. All their lives they had prayed
to have a son, and now they were old — too old to hope for a son.
"His name is to be John," he had written next. And then, with a
look of joy in his face, he had written: "He shall be great before
the Lord." But he had not tried to explain to her about the angel
Gabriel, who had told him these things, or about his own fear and
wonder, or about his words to the angel: "How shall I know this?
For I am an old man and my wife is advanced in years." These
mysteries were more than he could write upon his writing tablet,
but he often thought of them as the winter came and went and
the buds grew big on the trees in his garden. He was thinking of
them, in fact, on this bright spring day, as he sat under the
lemon tree.

Elizabeth was grinding barley inside the house. He could hear
the small mill going round and round. Good, patient Elizabeth, who
insisted on doing everything herself, even though she was growing old!

Suddenly his thoughts were interrupted by a knock at the door.
He sat up and listened. Elizabeth evidently had not heard, for she
was still turning the mill. There was another knock. He stood up
and went toward the house, but this time the mill stopped, and
he could hear his wife's slow, shuffling steps, moving toward the
door. The big bolt was pulled back, and the heavy door swung
open on its hinges. Then he heard a little cry of surprise. He hurried
into the house and through to the front door, and there stood
Elizabeth, with mingled surprise and fear and joy written all over
her wrinkled old face. Before her stood her cousin Mary from
Nazareth.

Elizabeth stood breathing very quickly. Then she called out in
a loud voice:

Blessed art thou among women and blessed is the fruit of thy
womb. . . .

She paused a moment, searching Mary's face. Then she went on more quietly:

And whence is this to me, that the mother of my Lord should come to me?

It was Mary's turn now to look startled. The mother of my Lord! Elizabeth knew! Somehow, she knew the secret about Jesus! God himself must have told her, for Mary had not spoken after her first greeting. But Elizabeth had not yet finished.

For behold, the moment the sound of thy greeting came to my ears, the babe in my womb leapt for joy. And blessed is she who has believed, because the things promised her by the Lord shall be accomplished.

Tears of joy ran down her wrinkled old face.

Mary stood very still, hearing and not hearing.

Suddenly, all the wonder and joy that had been growing in her ever since the angel's visit rushed to her lips in words. The wonder of God's goodness in choosing her, and the world's long yearning for a Redeemer, and all the aching hunger of the poor, crushed down by the proud and cruel, rushed out in a song like the songs of David which she used to sing in the Temple. But this was her song — and God's.

My soul doth magnify the Lord
And my spirit hath rejoiced in God my Saviour
Because he hath regarded the humility of his handmaid,
For behold henceforth all generations shall call me blessed
Because he that is mighty hath done great things to me
And holy is his name. . . .

He hath cast down the mighty from their seats
　　and he hath exalted the humble;
He hath filled the hungry with good things
　　and the rich he hath sent empty away. . . .

When Mary had finished her song, the two stood a moment in the open doorway, each blinded by her own vision. It was Elizabeth who spoke first. "Come," she said, laying her hand gently on Mary's shoulder, and she led her into the house.

Zachary was waiting for them just inside — Zachary who had been struck dumb. There were tears in his dim old eyes. He took Mary in his arms as a father would take his child and held her for a moment. Then he let go of her gently, almost with a kind of fear at having dared to touch her. He stood before her, trying to speak, his face working with the effort. Then, with a helpless look, he reached for his writing tablet. "Blessed be the Lord God of Israel," he wrote.

Mary never forgot the weeks that followed. They were filled with common things like weaving and sewing and grinding corn, but they were holy with expectation. The two mothers sat together in the late spring sunshine, sewing for the little sons that were to be born to them, talking of them, or thinking of them in silence. Sometimes Zachary sat nearby, with his writing tablet beside him and a faraway look in his eyes. And so spring turned into summer. The days grew long and warm, and the fruit ripened on the trees inside the garden. At last there came a day when there was a great bustle and stir in the big, square house. Neighbors leaned over their garden gates and said: "Elizabeth and Zachary have a son. He's a fine, strong boy, even though both the father and mother are old." Women came knocking at the door with gifts; men came to shake Zachary's hand and compliment him on having so fine a son. Zachary nodded and beamed; but still he could not speak. Instead he took his writing tablet and wrote: "Blessed be God."

On the eighth day, when the child was to receive his name, everyone was gathered in Zachary's house for the occasion. "Ah, but he's a fine boy," the women said; and the men, "He should be named Zachary for his father."

Zachary shook his head; he knew differently. The angel had told him what to name the child.

The relatives turned to Elizabeth. "His name shall be Zachary."

"No, John," she said, remembering what Zachary had written.

"But there is no one in the family of that name," the relatives argued. "Let it be Zachary."

Then Zachary reached for his writing tablet. Once again he wrote, as he had written for Elizabeth: "His name shall be John." Suddenly he felt his tongue loosen. Something inside of him was unlocked and he could speak. He stood up, his face flushed, his eyes shining. Everyone turned toward him in surprise. The words poured from him in a song of praise.

Blessed be the Lord God of Israel, because he hath visited and brought redemption for his people. . . .

He looked down at his little son, so strong and straight-limbed.

And thou, child, shalt be called the prophet of the Highest, for thou shalt go before the face of the Lord to prepare his ways. . . .

A few days later, Mary started back down the road from Ain-Karim, over the way she had come. Elizabeth did not need her any more, and it was time to be getting back to Nazareth. Zachary was riding beside her as far as the main road, where she would join a caravan going north. She knew what he would do after that. He would go to the Temple in Jerusalem and offer thanks to God for his son. His days were one constant song of praise.

She pondered over his words as she rode along beside him — those strange words he had spoken about little John: *And thou child shalt be called the prophet of the Highest, for thou shalt go before the face of the Lord to prepare his ways.* They were strange, mysterious words, but she knew they had something to do with Jesus. "God is very good," thought Mary, riding down the steep road on her donkey. "He is very, very good."

She would go back across Judea, across Samaria, across the level plain of Esdraelon, parched now with summer drought. She would go home and marry Joseph, and together they would wait for Jesus. When the figs had ripened, when the leaves had withered on the olive trees and the winter winds began to blow, he would be born. And the little child John some day would prepare his ways.

Chapter III

JESUS IS BORN IN BETHLEHEM

JOSEPH sent the hammer down with strong, even strokes. The nail was going through the wood slowly. It was hardwood — oak, the best kind for plowshares. When he had driven in the nail, he laid down the hammer and leaned with all his weight on the finished plow. It was sturdy and well built; it would cut a clean furrow — old Eli would be pleased. He ran his finger along the handles. He had sanded them smooth — they would not hurt old Eli's hands.

He stood the plow up in the corner and started to put away his tools. It was early winter and the days were growing short. It was too late now to begin something else. Besides, he was glad, these days, to go home a little early. Mary would be waiting, sitting in the half-light, with the supper set out on the table. She would have laid aside her sewing because of the growing darkness, but when he came, she would rise and light the lamp and bring him the little basin to purify his hands. Together they would stand to say the blessing that every Jewish man says before he eats: *Blessed art thou, O Lord our God, King of the Universe, who bringeth forth bread from the earth. . . .*

"I finished old Eli's plow," he would tell her. He knew what she would answer.

"I'll bake a loaf of bread for him tomorrow." Old Eli was poor and almost blind.

"You wait and see if he doesn't bring us a measure of barley when harvest comes," Joseph had said to Mary. Old Eli was like that — hating to receive without giving something in return.

Little did Joseph know that he and Mary would be many miles away when harvest came. . . .

With his tools put away, he picked up a broom and started to sweep the shavings from the floor of his shop. "You could eat off the floor in the shop of Joseph the carpenter," the neighbors used to say sometimes laughing. But it was one way to praise God — to do your work carefully.

Joseph was thinking of Jesus as he swept — Jesus who was now very soon to be born. All of his work now was for Jesus. He had made the house tight and warm for winter. He had carved a little cradle. Mary must have everything he could get for her . . . all fall he had worked and planned. Ah, Mary! How he loved the sound of her name! And to think God had given her to him, to guard and protect! Mary who was to be the mother of Jesus!

It was shortly before their marriage that the angel had come to him to tell him the secret about Mary. He had come to him in his sleep. "Do not be afraid, Joseph, Son of David," the angel had said, "to take Mary for thy wife, for that which is begotten of her is of the Holy Spirit. And she shall bring forth a Son, and thou shalt call his name Jesus, for he shall save his people from their sins. . . ."

Joseph had wakened trembling. *Thou shalt call his name Jesus. . . . He shall save the people from their sins.* . . . Those were the things one said of the Messias! He was afraid with a holy fear. He had risen from his bed, fearful and shaking, and had knelt down in the darkness to thank God. He had knelt there a long time. "Yes, Lord," he had said, not hearing the soft, night noises. "Make me worthy, Lord. . . ." The tears ran down his cheeks.

That was months ago. He was still praying the same prayer. . . . "Make me worthy, Lord."

Now, as he was sweeping, he was thinking of the words of the prophet Isaias:

> Behold a virgin shall conceive
> and bear a Son
> And his name shall be Emmanuel. . . .

Yet there was something strange about that prophecy, for it also said:

> And thou, Bethlehem,
> Out of thee shall come forth he
> that is to be the Ruler of Israel. . . .

Why did it not say Nazareth instead of Bethlehem? Yet if sometimes he secretly wondered, and Mary too, they never spoke about it. Who were they to question the words of the Holy Book? The prophets often spoke in hidden ways.

He swept the shavings neatly into a pile, and gathering them up, threw them in the fire. . . .

> And thou, Bethlehem
> Out of thee shall come forth he . . .

It was strange how those words haunted him tonight. He hung his work apron on a nail, covered over the fire for the night, wrapped his cloak about him, and opened the door of his shop. A gust of wind blew a swirl of dust into his eyes. But behind the sound of the wind, he could hear a confused murmur of many voices coming from the direction of the market place. He did not need to pass through the market on his way home — but he thought: Perhaps I should go and see what the noise is about. Nazareth was usually quiet at dusk on a winter day. . . .

He walked quickly down the street. As he neared the market place he could see an excited crowd elbowing and shoving. Soon he was caught up in its excited movement.

"Ah, neighbor Joseph, have you heard the news?"

"What news," Joseph asked quietly, trying to keep from being jostled.

"There was an edict — an edict from Caesar. There's to be a census. We are all to be enrolled. 'Each in his own city,' the edict said. Ah, but it's a hard thing to be traveling all about the country in the dead of winter — and the roads so bad, too."

"Yes, it will be hard for many," Joseph answered gently.

"What's your city, neighbor? Aren't you of the City of David?"

Joseph nodded. Yes, he was of the City of David. Both he and Mary were descended from the shepherd-king. . . . And the City of David was — Bethlehem.

Joseph shivered a little, as another gust of wind whipped open his cloak; but he smiled to himself ever so slightly.

"What are you smiling about, Joseph? It's no smiling matter, in the dead of winter, and my Sara with the cold ague upon her and me with a sore on my leg. What are you smiling about, Joseph?"

"Ah, I know, it is hard," Joseph repeated, but he was thinking:

> And thou, Bethlehem
> Out of thee shall come forth he
>   that is to be the Ruler of Israel. . . .

Mary sat with her sewing in her lap, waiting for Joseph to come. Joseph is late tonight, she thought. It was well she had left the broth on the stove, instead of dishing it up. It would have been quite cold by now. She sat very still, watching the shadows move across the wall, but her mind was elsewhere. Will it be this week or next? she thought. The kinswoman who was going to be with her when Jesus was born, as Mary had been with Elizabeth, had come to see her today. "I am ready," she had said, "when you need me. Send Joseph, and I will come." Now Mary, sitting in the growing dusk, was remembering the words of the angel:

> He shall be great, and shall be called the Son of the Most High . . .
> and of his kingdom there shall be no end. . . .

Just then she heard a familiar quick step on the path — Joseph was coming. She got up and lit the lamp and started toward the door to greet him. He opened it softly and came toward her. "Mary," he said, and then he was silent. He was thinking what it would mean to her — what it would mean to them both — to start out then for the long journey south to Bethlehem. In the corner, waiting and ready, stood the little crib he had made. Nearby, in a small wooden chest, were the tiny swaddling bands, the soft wool coverlets. Everything was ready for Jesus. Now there was no knowing what small, crowded village inn would be his birthplace. "Mary, can you bear hard news?"

She listened quietly. Then suddenly, her face lighted with a strange look of wonder. He guessed the thought that was passing in her mind.

> And thou, Bethlehem
> Out of thee shall come forth he
> that is to be the Ruler of Israel. . . .

*   *   *

Two days later Mary and Joseph started down through the town to join a caravan going south. Mary was on the donkey which had carried her that spring to Ain-Karim. In her saddlebags were the tiny swaddling bands, the white wool coverlets; but the cradle stood in the empty house. Joseph walked beside her on foot.

"Ah, neighbor Joseph, you wasted no time in getting started. I see your Mary is with you. My Sara is staying behind."

"God be with you, neighbor. You are ready early."

They were a friendly group, these Nazarenes, and Joseph returned their friendliness. But he was glad for the moments of silence that came as they wound their way around mudholes in the storm-washed road. He kept watching Mary anxiously, for the road was hard and rough in winter. After the first half day, her face looked white and drawn, but she made no murmur. She smiled at him with her shy, knowing smile. . . .

> And thou Bethlehem
> Out of thee . . .

It was their secret. The tiredness did not matter.

They rode across the plains of Esdraelon — but now they were bleak and cold; and then they crossed the country of Samaria; and then, on the third day, they entered Judea. But the olive trees were bare and the hillsides were gaunt and brown. It was well along in the fourth day that they drew near the holy city of Jerusalem, where the rest of the caravan was going.

"Shall we stay tonight in Jerusalem?" Joseph asked.

"No, let us go on," Mary said. Her face was white, but she smiled as she said it. It would be good to be at their journey's end. And so, they skirted the city on the west without entering the gates, and headed south the four miles to Bethlehem. They went along in silence, busy with their thoughts. A little while before Mary had said, "I think it will be tonight, Joseph. I think Jesus will be coming tonight." Her voice was full of joy.

"Is there a good inn at Bethlehem?" Joseph asked a traveler as they paused to rest by Rachel's tomb.

"Yes, sir, yes. It's at the crossroads, just as you come into town. God be with you, sir."

They were nearly there by now, and the air was frosty and cold as they wound their way along the narrow ridge of the Judean hills. Far below them, on the plains of Moab, the rich red earth was turning dark with nightfall. Above them the first faint stars were showing in the sky. Shepherds had gathered their sheep together for the night and were lighting fires on the hillsides. Some were already seated, watching the sparks fly upward, laughing and talking and playing on their pipes.

> Tu-la-la-ru
> Tu-la-ru-la-la-ru . . .

It was a wistful, haunting little sound. Mary and Joseph smiled as they listened. Shepherds were kindly people; they loved their sheep. David had been a shepherd before he had been a king. Hundreds of years before he had said in one of his songs that God was like a shepherd — it was a nice thought.

> Tu-la-la-ru-la-ru . . .

Joseph's feet were cut with stones and brambles, and Mary was so tired that she ached in every bone. But they did not speak of these things. Bethlehem was just ahead. They had caught glimpses of it now and then, with its white roofs and its twinkling lights, as the road wound back and forth around the edges of the hills. It was with great relief that they rounded the last bend and came into the outskirts of the town. They quickened their pace a little — the inn could not be far away. But the town was not the quiet little place it was in normal times. There were shouts, and the noise of donkeys moving about in courtyards, and the high-pitched jingle of camel bells. There were many, it seemed, who had come to the City of David to be enrolled.

When they turned in at the innyard, they could see already that the inn was crowded. Donkeys were jostling one another; camel drivers were shouting and scolding; boys were hurrying about with bags of feed and water for the drinking trough. Inside, there was noisy laughter. They were not surprised when the innkeeper thrust out his head in answer to their knock. "No room in the inn. You'll have to go somewhere else." They were not surprised, but they were very tired, and they shrank from the uproar and bustle of the town.

Joseph helped Mary gently back onto her donkey, and they started on their fruitless search, knocking at doors, speaking to people on street corners.

"Could you tell us where we might find a night's lodging? The inn is full."

"Sorry, sir — we've no room here. You might try in the next street — the third house — they sometimes take travelers."

"Please, we were told at this house you might have room for us to spend the night."

"Sorry, we just took in guests."

It was quite dark now, and Mary was shivering with the cold.

"Here, take my cloak," Joseph said, but she would not hear of it. They paused a moment to consider. Where could they try next?

Suddenly, Mary felt a slight pull on her sleeve.

"Lady," a boy's voice said, "I know a place."

She looked down into the serious, upturned face of a ragged boy.

"You do, son?"

"Yes, lady, it's not a very nice place, but I heard you talking. It's the only place, lady, and there's straw to lie on. Everything else is full."

She turned to Joseph, and he nodded.

"All right, son," Joseph said. "You lead the way."

And so they set out together in the winter night — the ragged boy and the man and woman from the north. "She looks very tired," thought the boy, "and yet she isn't cross — and she has the loveliest smile. And the man is kind and gentle."

He led them along a rocky path that followed the edge of the hill. Wind stung their faces, and it was hard to see where they were going, once they had left the town. But it was really not very far. They had hardly gone a quarter of an hour when the boy stopped and cried, "There it is," and he pointed to a cave cut into the side of the hill. He led them to it and pushed open the rough wooden door. "See, it is quite large — and it has nice straw in it." He looked at them anxiously. "Will it be all right?" It was low and dark and damp, with a rough manger at the back, but it was quite clean for a stable.

"Of course it's all right," Joseph said, and Mary, tired as she was, nodded and smiled. The boy stood there a moment, eyeing her wistfully. She was such a young, lovely lady! "God be with you," he said shyly, and darted out into the night.

*   *   *

On one of the steep ridges above Bethlehem, shepherds were sleeping around a fire. Only one was awake — a tall young lad in a rough shepherd's tunic. It was his turn to watch, and he sat by the fire, trying to keep awake. He amused himself by counting the sparks, and then he shifted his position and looked up at the stars. They made him think of a line from a song of the shepherd-king David:

> The heavens shew forth the glory of God
> and the firmament declareth the work of his hands. . . .

He fingered his pipe as he sat there, wishing he could play a tune. But of course he couldn't — it would wake the others.

Just beyond the circle of light, the sheep were huddled together, sleeping. They were his charge for the night and they must come to no harm. He scrambled to his feet and tiptoed over to count them — they were all there. He tiptoed back and stood a minute, scanning the dark hills for signs of danger before settling down again. Suddenly a light attracted him over to one side, and he gave a quick little cry.

Instantly the others sprang up. "What is it, lad? Is it a wolf?"

"Look!" cried the boy. "Look over there!" And he pointed. But where before he had seen only a light, now there was the figure of a man, all shining and radiant, standing in the midst of the brightness. With one impulse, they fell upon their faces. They were shaking with fear.

The figure came closer. "Fear not," he said, and his voice was kind and comforting. Still trembling, they looked at him, their eyes growing used to the brightness. Could this be an angel on their cold, rocky hillside? Could an angel be speaking to them? Down in the market place, people stepped aside to avoid them, and they always sat in the very last seats in the Synagogue on the Sabbath, because of their ragged clothes. Surely, an angel would not be coming to them. There must be some mistake.

But there was no mistake. An angel from heaven had a message for them from the Most High God! They were simple enough to listen. It would be no use to go telling the Scribes and Pharisees in Jerusalem that the Son of God was born that night in a stable. It would be no use to tell Herod or Caesar. Yes, it was to shepherds God had sent his messenger. When they were calm enough to listen, he began:

Fear not, for behold I bring you tidings of great joy which shall be to all the people. For this day is born to you a Saviour who is Christ the Lord, in the City of David. And this shall be a sign unto you. You will find the Infant wrapped in swaddling-clothes, and laid in a manger.

The shepherds listened on their knees, their poor hearts beating wildly. The angel had hardly finished speaking when they heard all around them the most wonderful singing — hundreds and hundreds of voices of angelic sweetness, all singing together:

> Glory to God in the highest
> and peace on earth
> to men of good will.

Gradually the voices grew fainter, the brightness faded. A shivering little band of shepherds knelt trembling in the darkness, alone once more on their hillside.

At first they were too dazed to move or speak. They knelt on, staring into the darkness, with the words of the angel echoing in their ears:

> And this shall be a sign unto you. You will find the Infant wrapped in swaddling-clothes and laid in a manger . . .
> Good tidings of great joy . . .
> A Saviour who is Christ the Lord . . .

Suddenly the full truth dawned on them: It was the Messias — at last he had come! They might be poor, stupid shepherds, but they too had heard the prophecies, sitting in the last seats in the Synagogue: He was to be called *Wonderful, Counselor, God the Mighty, Prince of Peace* . . .

"Brothers," said one of the shepherds softly, when at last they were able to speak, "we must go and find the Child. We must look for the Baby in swaddling clothes, lying in a manger."

"I'll take him my sheepskin," said one.

"And I this loaf of bread," announced another.

"And I this copper coin," said a third.

"And I my pipe," thought the shepherd boy who had been the first one to see the angel. But he was too shy to speak. He fingered it under his cloak — it was the dearest thing he had.

And so they started down the rocky trail. When they reached the main road, they paused bewildered. Was no one else going to seek the Child? There was not a soul abroad. Surely the angel would have told them, down in the town. Why was not the road full of people, going to find the little King?

They hesitated, wondering which way to go. A Baby lying in a manger! There were many mangers in Bethlehem. At least half the houses in town would have courtyards with a manger in them! As they stood there puzzled, one of them cried out, "Brothers, look! — over there!" They looked where he pointed. They spied, very low in the sky, almost touching the ridge opposite, the brightest star they had ever seen. They rubbed their eyes and looked again. It was brighter than ever, and it seemed almost to be beckoning them. Without thinking, they started walking toward it, scrambling up the steep, rocky ridge.

Suddenly, one of them called out: "The cave — it's leading us to the cave!"

They knew that cave well — and in it they knew that there was a manger. They hurried now eagerly, stumbling over rocks and brambles. . . .

> For behold I bring you tidings of great joy
> which shall be to all the people. . . .

They were breathless when they reached the top of the slope. They were almost at the entrance of the cave — and the star was standing still now — very, very bright — directly over their heads.

They waited outside a moment to catch their breath. They straightened their poor, ragged clothes and shook the dust from their sandals. Then, taking their gifts in their hands, they stooped one by one and entered.

Inside they saw — a man, a lady, a donkey, and, yes, a Baby, lying on straw in the manger. Everything was just as the angel had said — simple, and plain — and beautiful. Suddenly they began to tremble. Tears rushed into their eyes and down their wind-burned cheeks. It is strange, they thought, to be crying about a Baby!

They stood there for a moment, unnoticed. Presently, the lady looked up and gave a little start of surprise. "Joseph," she said, and the man got up and came toward them. His eyes too were wet, but he was smiling.

"May the dear God be praised," said the oldest shepherd, and he bowed deeply and laid down his sheepskin. "It's not very much, but it will keep him warm."

"The blessing of the Lord be on him," said another, setting down his loaf of bread. Last of all came the shepherd boy with his pipe, but he was too shy to say anything at all. The Child slept on, untroubled, wrapped in his swaddling clothes, the little Saviour who was Christ the Lord.

"Look," the lady said, going over and lifting the tiny coverlet. She pulled out a small, curled hand. It opened and closed about her finger, and dark eyes opened for a moment; then they closed again. "His name is Jesus," she said very softly.

The shepherds came forward shyly. "Ah, Lady, may we touch him? May we touch the little Jesus?"

She nodded, and they stroked his soft cheeks with their big, roughened hands. They kissed his tiny hand, his swaddling bands, his little coverlet; and then they turned and kissed the lady's robe. For a moment they stood shyly, feasting their eyes.

Finally one of them said, "Brothers, let us go. We must tell the people of Bethlehem that they too may adore him." They bowed, one after another, and tiptoed out. The first light of dawn was in the east, but the bright star was still there, shining above the doorway to the cave.

> Glory to God in the Highest
> and on earth, peace
> to men of Good Will. . . .

They would never forget this night as long as they lived.

It was still early when they reached the market place. Most of the townspeople were snoring in their beds, but a few energetic venders were already at their stalls, laying out their wares.

"Have you seen the little King?" called out one of the shepherds.

"The little king?" echoed the vender. He had a cross, dark face.

"Yes, the little King, the Saviour God has promised. Didn't the angel bring you the good news?"

A small crowd gathered quickly, in spite of the early hour. Some looked interested, but others started jeering: "What kind of wine were you drinking on your hillside to be talking about seeing a king!"

Sadly the shepherds shook their heads. Would nobody believe them?

"We drank no wine. We were asleep till the angels came and woke us."

But the crowd would not listen to them. "Be gone, fellows. We have no time for shepherds' tales."

And so the shepherds gathered their cloaks around them and made their way out of the town. They went back silently to their hillside, to their cottages, their sheep. Their wives would believe them, their children, their children's children. Years hence they would still be telling, around their watch fires, the story of the angels and the cave, of the Infant in swaddling clothes laid in a manger — the tidings of great joy.

Chapter IV

JESUS VISITS HIS FATHER'S HOUSE

THERE was not much going on one wintry day in the great Temple at Jerusalem. The Morning Sacrifice was over, and the marble pavements were washed clean. The fires on the great stone altars smoldered slowly. All but a few of the priests had gone about their business, and the Temple guards slouched sleepily at their posts.

Few people moved about in the Temple Court that time of year. It was not near the time of any of the great feasts. Lepers coming to show themselves to the priests as the law required and men bringing sin offerings made up the chief number. There was always a certain number of mothers bringing their first-born sons to be presented to the Lord. And of course there were the faithful ones, like Anna, who stayed in the Temple night and day, and old Simeon who came tottering up the steps each morning. The guards stood respectfully at attention when he passed. He spent long hours praying for the coming of the Messias, and it was said that the Lord had promised him he should not die till his hope was fulfilled. His favorite prayer was the Kaddish. Over and over he said it:

Magnified and sanctified be his great name. . . . May he establish his kingdom during your life and during your days. . . .

29

The outer Court was quiet too. The sellers of sacrificial animals
had let their stocks get low. There was no need to replenish them
till nearer the Passover season. Even the money-changers came
strolling in late to their tables. They lounged in their places, hardly
noticing a couple who crossed the courtyard — a man in the clothes
of a Galilean workman and a dark-eyed girl of a mother carrying
a sleeping child. They headed toward the booth of a ragged old
woman with doves in a rickety cage. She was dozing, but she woke
with a start and smiled a toothless smile.

"One dove, my pretty, or two?" The rich took a dove and a lamb
for their offering, the poor two doves.

It was the man who answered. "Two," he said quietly.

"Ah, yes, two doves," echoed the old woman amiably. "Two for
the likes of us. May I see the child? He's a lovely boy, my pretty —
and very like his mother." She opened the cage and thrust in her
bony hands. The birds clucked and fluttered.

"Here, Sir," she said. The man took them gently, and they lay
very still in his hands, looking about with beady eyes. The old
woman pocketed the coin he gave her, but there was a wistful look
in her eyes. "Good day. May the God of Israel bless you." She
watched them as they moved across the court. Then she settled
down for another nap.

Once inside the spacious Court of the Women, the couple looked
about and then headed toward an attendant who was leaning
against a pillar. The man straightened up as they approached. There
was no need to tell him what they wanted. A man with two
doves and a woman carrying a baby wanted only one thing.

"You'll have to wait," he said. "There's no priest free just now."
But as he looked at the mother's face, a memory stirred in his
mind. Where had he seen her before? It was not a face one
forgot. But he could not remember where he had seen it. No
matter — he saw many faces in the course of a year!

"The father's name?" he asked mechanically.

The man hesitated; then he said: "Joseph — Joseph of Nazareth,
the son of Jacob, of the house of David."

"And the mother's name?"

"Mary of Nazareth, the daughter of Joachim, also of the house of David."

"And the child's?"

"Jesus."

"Born in Nazareth?"

"No, in Bethlehem."

"Wait here." He pointed to a stone bench, and started toward the Court of the Israelites. It was strange how he could not get that face out of his mind!

Mary and Joseph sat down and waited. Jesus slept peacefully in Mary's arms, and the doves were quiet in Joseph's hands. Only the tap-tap of sandaled feet on marble floors broke the silence, as people moved to and fro, dropping their coins in the alms boxes, or made their way to the Treasury or the Council Chamber. Now and then there came a faint drone of treble voices — the little boys in the Temple School were reciting their lessons. It made Mary smile to hear them. The sounds and the sharp odor of incense brought back a flood of memories. For a moment she was a little girl again, praying by her bed, sitting at her loom, peering through the latticed window at the holy mysteries at the hour of Morning Sacrifice. Then Jesus stirred in her arms and she was back in the present again.

Jesus had come for the first time into the Temple. He had come into his Father's House. Today she was going to offer him to God. . . .

He shall be called great, and shall be called the Son of the Most High, and the Lord God will give him the throne of David. . . .

He was still sleeping, warm and flushed, in her arms.

Presently the attendant returned. "The priest is ready," he said. "Will you come this way?" He led them to the broad marble stairs that ascended to the Court of the Israelites. "You stand on the top step," he said, and left them.

Mary's heart beat more quickly as she climbed the great stone stairs. God had not seemed so close since the day of the angel's visit. Tears blurred her eyes as she stood before the gold and silver gate of Nicanor, through which no woman might ever pass. In a moment the priest of the Most High God would come and take her Child in his arms and bless him. The priest would not know that he was different from other children unless God told him. But she and God would know. . . .

> Behold the handmaid of the Lord.
> Be it done unto me according to thy word. . . .

Today she was renewing that promise. She was giving to God his only Son. She stood on the top step, holding her Child against her. She could feel the beating of his heart.

Suddenly there was the sound of footsteps coming toward her, the soft rustle of stiff linen vestments, a slight, wheezing cough. She looked up and saw that the priest was there. His face was vaguely familiar. She must have seen him sometimes in the long line of priests waiting for the sound of the trumpet at the Hour of Sacrifice.

First he said the prayers of purification over her bowed head, speaking rapidly in a low voice. Then he took the Child from her arms; he raised up Jesus, offering him to the Lord, saying the age-old prayers. His face was dark, impassive. This was just one more first-born son of a young Jewish mother. He did not know the secret.

When he had finished the prayers, he gave back Jesus to Mary. He lifted his hands and gave them both the blessing. Then with a nod he turned and went back to the Court of the Priests. Joseph handed the doves to a Temple attendant, and the little ceremony was over.

For a moment Mary did not move. She was too lost in prayer. . . . "My soul doth magnify the Lord," she was thinking, "and my spirit hath rejoiced in God my Saviour. . . ." But then Jesus stirred in her arms, and she was called back from her thoughts. He was awake now, gazing about with a look of wonder. It was only then she realized that the priest had gone. She turned slowly on the step, and as she did so, she heard someone coming across the pavement with a slow, shuffling gait toward the stairs. There was the tapping of a cane moved haltingly. She knew that sound. As a child in the Temple she had heard it often. "That's Simeon, my darling," Anna used to say, stopping her loom to listen. "That's Simeon coming to pray for the dear Messias. Shall we stop a moment and say the Kaddish?" Together they would pause and say it as the old steps shuffled past. "There aren't many in Israel as holy as Simeon," Anna used to say with a sigh as she turned back to her weaving. "Surely God will listen to his prayers."

Coming down the stairs with Joseph just behind her, Mary could see the stooped old figure coming toward her. The shuffling steps came nearer. She paused at the bottom of the stairway and waited. Jesus was awake and seemed to be trying to follow the old man with his eyes. She loosened his coverlet and lifted him up a little. The old man stopped abruptly, and the dim old eyes came suddenly alive. The wrinkled hands reached forward and took the Child from her arms. The old voice called out clearly:

Now Thou dost dismiss Thy servant, O Lord, according to Thy
    word in peace
Because my eyes have seen Thy salvation which Thou hast pre-
    pared before the face of all peoples . . .
A light to the revelation of the Gentiles and the glory of Thy
    people Israel. . . .

At first he hardly seemed to notice Mary; his whole attention was focused on the Child. Then suddenly he turned to her. His face was gentle yet stern.

Behold this Child is set for the fall and resurrection of many
    in Israel
And thy own soul a sword shall pierce that out of many hearts
    thoughts may be revealed.

He spoke the last words almost fiercely, but it was the fierceness of love. Then suddenly he was a weak old man again with dim eyes and shaking hands. He stood by the steps, swaying under the weight of the Child. Mary took Jesus back into her arms, and Simeon turned slowly, feebly, from her. Leaning more heavily than ever on his cane, he went shuffling off across the Court. The tears were streaming down his kind old face.

Mary stood trembling at the foot of the great staircase, holding Jesus tightly in her arms. God had told the secret to Simeon — now he could die in peace. But those were strange words he said:

This Child is set for the rise and fall of many. . . .
And thy own soul a sword shall pierce. . . .

She stood a moment as though dazed. Then gently Joseph took her by the arm. "Come," he said, leading her toward the bench. "You must rest a moment, and then we will look for Anna." But she had gone only a few steps when she heard a little cry of surprise behind her. Turning around, they saw the old form of Anna hurrying toward them, her wrinkled face smiling, her thin arms outstretched.

"Mary," she said making as though to fold her in her arms. Then suddenly she stopped short and turned very pale. She swayed a little, then steadied herself and cried out in a loud voice: "The redemption of Israel is at hand!" People turned and stared at the little group and started toward them. "Do you not see that the hour of the Lord is at hand?" she said as the people pressed around her. "Blessed be the Lord God of Israel." But they could make nothing of her words. All they saw was a very young mother with a baby and a man dressed as a Galilean workman. "She has seen some vision," they said to one another. "Anna has seen some vision." And soon the small group scattered again.

Presently Anna grew quiet, but the tears ran down her wrinkled old face. "Ah, my Child! God heard our prayers, yours and mine. Now I must go to my loom and my prayers, but the blessing of God go with you. Forgive an old woman her tears!" She kissed Mary and then she paused. "Dare I kiss the holy little One?"

Mary could hardly find words to speak, but she lifted up the little Jesus. Anna kissed the small, moist forehead, and turning, went through the curtained door.

Mary was silent as she walked beside Joseph through the great bronze gates of the Temple into the outer court. He was carrying Jesus now, very gently. The dark eyes were open, gazing sweetly and soberly about. It was midmorning, and the streets were filling with people — women going to market, men bent on business, Pharisees hurrying to the Temple. Mary kept close to Joseph, but her thoughts were far away. She did not see the people. She saw only Simeon holding up her Child and speaking his burning words:

> He shall be for the fall and resurrection of many. . . .
> And thy own soul a sword shall pierce. . . .

Chapter V

JESUS GOES DOWN INTO EGYPT

HE Jewish colonies in the cities of northern Egypt were friendly places. Fellow countrymen in a foreign land cling together, and Jews are a clannish people. The Egyptian Jews had their own markets, their own craftsmen, their rabbis, their holydays, their Synagogues. Yet they never inquired into each other's secrets or asked why others had left their native country and traveled down through miles of barren desert into this foreign land.

Neighbors did not inquire of the carpenter Joseph why he and his young wife Mary and their little son Jesus had come out of the land of their birth. Yet there were rumors that they had fled from Bethlehem when King Herod ordered the boy babies killed.

It was a memory Mary and Joseph tried to forget. It all began with the visit of the three kings. They were not exactly kings but wise men — the Romans called them *Magi*. But the people of Bethlehem thought they were kings as they looked out of their doorways and saw them climbing down from their camels. "Look," the children shouted, running to their mothers. "Did you ever see such splendid clothes!" But the smaller children cried to see their dark foreign faces and black beards. "Hush, children, do not cry," their mothers told them. "Hush, don't you cry."

Mary and Joseph were living in a small house in the lower part of town, near the street of the carpenters where Joseph worked. Jesus was playing on the floor on a little coverlet, and Mary was grinding corn. Suddenly she heard a knock at the door. She opened it hesitantly. They were strangers in town, and not many came to their door. Three men stood on the doorstep in silk and velvet robes, carrying carved boxes. They were like something out of a story.

Mary took a quick step backward and looked at them, bewildered — Mary who was only fifteen. The three strangers bowed low. "We have come out of the East," one of them said in a strange, foreign accent. "We were led here by a star to worship a king. Herod's counselors directed us to Bethlehem, and the star stopped over this house."

Mary, still wondering, led them in. "Here is Jesus," she said simply, picking him up from the floor. She was thinking: He *is* a king, for the angel said:

He shall be king over the house of Jacob forever,
And of his kingdom there shall be no end.

Jesus reached out his tiny hands. He looked like any Jewish baby.

The strangers fell on their knees. "May the God of Israel be praised," one of them said. "We worshiped other gods in our own lands, but this is a great wonder."

"Aye, Lady, it is a wonderful thing that one so tiny should be so great," said a second.

"Our wisdom is nothing," the third one said, shaking his head — "all nothing. This Little One has what we never were able to find."

Mary marveled at so much faith. She remembered Simeon's words: *Behold this Child is set for the fall and rise of many.* He was already raising up the hearts of these three men.

After a moment one of the strangers said in his queer accent: "We have brought him gifts. Would you deign to accept them?" They opened their fine carved boxes and brought out gold, frankincense, and myrrh. They were strange gifts for a baby — but quite fitting for a king. Mary sat holding Jesus. It was all like a very strange dream.

They knelt down then on the bare earth floor as courtiers kneel to kings. They kissed the hands of Jesus, the feet, the tiny linen tunic, the soft, silky hair, and they kissed the white hands of Mary. Then they gravely took their leave. "We have found what we sought," they said. "We know what greatness is. It is a vision hard to keep."

"Yes," said Mary gently. "May the blessing of God go with you."

"May the blessing of God remain with you," they answered.

They stepped out into the narrow street and threaded their way to the place where their camels were tied. People looked out of their doorways and stared. "It's the kings again," the children cried. But the memory was soon blotted out by a dreadful and tragic event. The three kings, as was said, had stopped in Jerusalem to inquire where the Child might be. Since they were asking for a king, they inquired at the palace of the king — the palace of King Herod.

"What's this!" he exclaimed angrily. "Did they say there is a newborn king? There shall be no king but Herod."

"Perhaps they were speaking of the Messias," one of his counselors said. But that did not lessen his anger. Calling his counselors and scribes together, he asked, "Where do the Scriptures say the Messias is to be born?"

"In Bethlehem, your Highness."

Then let all the boy babies in Bethlehem be killed."

"How old, your Highness?"

"Ah, well, let's see — all under two."

"It shall be done, your Highness."

Mad, jealous, sick old Herod gave his cruel command, but it did not work. The boy babies in Bethlehem were slain, but Jesus was not among them. He was already fleeing in his mother's arms to Egypt. God had seen to that. He had sent an angel to Joseph to warn him in his sleep:

Arise and take the Child and his mother and fly into Egypt, and be there until I shall tell thee. For it will come to pass that Herod will seek the Child to destroy him.

Joseph had wakened Mary and they had fled with the sleeping Jesus. They were well out of town when the soldiers began their work. They pressed on as fast as they could, choosing the least-traveled roads.

"Can you go on further?" Joseph asked Mary gently as they came toward nightfall to some crossroads inn.

"Yes, Joseph," she answered quietly, but her face was white and drawn. She shifted the sleeping Child in her arms and moistened his parched little lips. "Yes, of course I can go on."

Day after day they traveled, and at last they crossed the border into Egypt. Only then did they begin to feel safe. They sought out the nearest Jewish settlement, and soon they were a part of that small, transplanted Jewish world. It was so alike and yet so different from the world they had left behind them. Joseph worked in his shop; Mary wove and sewed, ground corn, and swept the floor. Together they prayed the same prayers — the Songs of David, the Kaddish, the Eighteen Benedictions. But when they chanted, "I will lift up my eyes unto the hills," reciting the prayers of their people, their eyes searched in vain the sun-scorched Egyptian horizon. There were no hills to be seen, but only the pointed pyramids, outlined against the burning sky.

Jesus grew strong and brown, and when winter came he took his first steps. "Come, Jesus," Joseph coaxed, and he came staggering and stumbling across the floor like any child learning to walk. He sat for hours on the workshop floor, playing with the curly shavings. Sometimes he sat on Mary's lap. "Pretty," he said, touching her long, dark hair, and "Mother." She kissed the small brown hands. She was not yet seventeen.

So the months passed, and Bethlehem seemed very far away. Nazareth seemed almost like a dream. People said of Joseph, "He's a good workman," and they brought him many orders. And of Mary they said, "She's a dear one, this little mother," and they sent for her when their children fell ill. As for Jesus — they paused as they passed the open doorway to watch him at his play.

"Doesn't he ever cry?" they asked Mary.

"No, he never does," she answered, and she picked him up and kissed him, thinking her hidden thoughts. She was recalling Simeon's words:

This Child is set for the rise and fall of many. . . .
And thy own soul a sword shall pierce. . . .

But the very next day he cried — when he saw someone beating a camel. It was the first of his small sorrows. Gradually they taught him to say his prayers. He advanced in wisdom with the years and in favor with God and with men.

Then one night Joseph had another dream. The angel appeared to him again and said:

Arise and take the Child, and go into the land of Israel. For they are dead that sought the death of the Child.

Joseph woke Mary and told her.

"Yes," she answered simply. She was growing used to these strange commands. Yet when pieced together, they matched the prophecies perfectly. There was an old sentence in Scripture which read: Out of Egypt have I called my Son.

"Are you leaving us, neighbors?" people asked them as they saw them packing their things. "Are you going back home again to Israel? God speed you on your way." But they asked no questions.

They would miss the tall carpenter and his shy, kind young wife, and his joyous little boy. They stood waving good-by with longing in their eyes when the little group set out to join a north-bound caravan for home. Someday they too might return to the land of their birth. "God speed you, neighbors."

"Shall we go back to Bethlehem or to Nazareth?" Joseph asked Mary as they traveled north over the hot sands. But she left the choice to him. She and Jesus were in his hands — and God's. He prayed and decided on Bethlehem — it was nearer the Holy City.

Slowly they went across the sands of Egypt into the rocky pastures of Judea. Bethlehem was not very far beyond. They spent the night in one of those crossroads inns which were built at intervals along the caravan routes. It was little more than a shelter from the rain.

They were lying on mats in an open porchlike place, thatched with dry palm branches. Jesus and Mary slept, but Joseph tossed and turned, for a voice kept whispering in his ear: *Do not go to Bethlehem. Herod indeed is dead, but his son is reigning. It is not safe for the Child.*

Joseph stirred and rose up on his elbow. He looked over ' at Mary — Mary who was not yet twenty, asleep like a child, wrapped in her blue mantle. Jesus was asleep beside her, his tiny hand closed about her sleeve. Joseph leaned on his elbow for a time, watching them. At last he lay back on his mat and fell asleep.

The next morning he said to Mary: "We must go to Nazareth. Bethlehem is not safe."

She nodded and smiled her shy, secret smile.

There was an old saying: *"He shall be called a Nazarene."*

A few weeks later there was a new topic of conversation in Nazareth.

"Have you heard about Joseph and Mary? You know — Joseph the carpenter, and Mary who lived as a child in the Temple. They're back again, after all this time."

"Are they indeed! And have they any children?"

"One child — a son — Jesus. He's the sturdiest, prettiest child I've seen in a long time. He plays about in Joseph's shop."

Soon the topic lost its novelty. People got used to seeing the tall young carpenter back again in his shop, with the little boy playing at his feet. They got used to seeing his young girl-wife at the well, waiting her turn. They became once more Joseph and Mary and Jesus *of Nazareth.* They were a part of that small, friendly world.

Chapter VI

JESUS IS LOST FOR THREE DAYS

HE Nazareth pilgrims straggled along wearily at the end of their first day's journey. They had been to Jerusalem for the Feast of the Passover and now they were on their way home. The caravan had been late that morning in starting. One woman wanted to stop at the bazaar, another had to get a sandal mended, a man wanted ointment for a sore. But at last they were all assembled.

They had walked rapidly at first, but they slackened their pace toward noon. Now they were straggling along in little groups, the women and girls together, the men ahead, the boys by themselves, now racing ahead, now lagging behind.

Mary, the mother of Jesus, was with the women — Mary who was not yet thirty. She was only half listening to their chatter. The talk was of sewing and cooking and troubles with growing boys. Other women's sons, it seemed, were ever getting into mischief — running away from the Synagogue School and stealing the neighbors' ripe figs. Mary smiled to herself, thinking how different it was with Jesus. He was twelve now, tall and tanned and sturdy. She thought of their days together — the sweet, unhurried days.

Jesus was always the first one up in the morning. He lit the fire

42

for her, brought in the water, and turned the little mill when her hands grew tired, though most boys would have called these tasks women's work. Then, when these were done, he went to the shop to help Joseph. She thought of the proud light in Joseph's eyes as he watched the boy planing the wood so straight and smooth! "He's a better carpenter than I already," Joseph said fondly. Jesus worked so quickly, so quietly, without any fuss or stir! He learned other things quickly too, this son of hers — this Son of God. When he was still quite small he could say the Eighteen Benedictions and long passages of the Torah by heart.

Now he was twelve, and Joseph had said to him one day that spring: "Son, in one more year you will come under the Law. It is time you began to observe its precepts. This year you may make the Passover Pilgrimage."

Jesus had flushed with happiness, but as the time drew near, he had seemed more quiet than usual. Often in the evening, he climbed the hill above the house and sat looking far out over the valley. When he came home she could tell by his face he had been praying. There were already secret places in his mind which she did not try to enter. He was her son, simple and young and good — but she never forgot that he was also the Son of God.

She was thinking of these things as the party straggled along at the end of its first day's journey. The travelers stopped at sundown to pitch camp for the night. She was not surprised that she did not see Jesus. He was with the boys, of course, foraging for firewood. Presently he would be along with his arms full of twigs and branches. She set about with the other women unpacking the bread and cheese and figs for supper, while the men strung up blankets on poles for shelter.

One by one the boys came scrambling down the slope with their loads of faggots. The men made a fire, and people began to gather together in families. They stood facing toward Jerusalem to say the blessing:

Blessed art thou, O Lord . . . who bringeth forth bread from the earth. . . .

Then they sat down to eat. But Jesus was not there. He did not come carrying firewood, or bringing water from the well. He was not anywhere to be found. Joseph went about from group to group. "Have you seen Jesus? He isn't here."

"No, Joseph, no. We haven't seen him."

"Boys, did you see Jesus?"

"No, sir. He wasn't with us."

"Not all day?"

"No, sir, no."

"But where — " Yes, where was Jesus?

"Tomorrow we will go back and look," Joseph said gently to Mary, trying to reassure her. It was out of the question to go back that night. One could not travel after dark over those mountain roads. Looking at Mary, standing white-faced beside him, her hands clasped tightly, he thought of Simeon's words: *And thy own soul a sword shall pierce.* It was pierced now surely.

People pressed around her kindly. "Ah, my poor one, sit down and take a cup of this broth. . . ." "The good God will protect him. . . ." "Tomorrow you will find him. He will be at the house of friends. . . ." They were good people, these neighbors of Nazareth.

"Thank you, neighbors," Mary answered, trying to keep her voice steady. "Thank you for your kind words." She was glad when they had finished eating and could settle down for the night. But as she lay that night in her improvised tent, sleep did not come. Where, oh where was Jesus? *"Hear, O God, my supplication,"* she prayed in the words of King David. *"Be attentive to my prayer."*

They started back the next morning almost before it was light. Whenever they passed a traveler they asked, "Have you seen Jesus? He is twelve, but tall for his age. He was wearing a brown tunic — the kind we wear in Galilee — and carrying a large leather pouch." But nobody had seen him.

It was late in the day when they entered the city. They had friends in the lower part of town, near the Garden of Gethsemani, and they went there first, but Jesus was not there. "What! Is he lost?" they exclaimed. "We have seen nothing of him. But you must stay with us till you find him, and we will help you search."

They had other friends up near the market place. They went there next, but Jesus was not there. They looked in the street of the carpenters, in the market, in the Garden of Gethsemani — everywhere they could think of. That night again they tossed and turned without sleeping. "Hear, O God, my supplication," Mary prayed again, and Joseph prayed also.

"Joseph," Mary said the next morning, "before we look further, shall we go to the Temple to pray?" And so together they climbed the steep streets to the Temple Esplanade. It was still quite crowded from the Passover. Venders were shouting their wares; money-changers were stacking their coins; sheep were bleating; people were all talking at once. Joseph and Mary were glad to escape from the noise into the quiet court inside. There, in the Court of the Women, one could think and pray.

They rested for a few minutes on one of the stone benches, listening to the far-off drone of voices. *"I cried to the Lord with my voice; with my voice I made supplication"* prayed Mary in the words of another of David's Psalms. Presently Joseph got up and went over to drop an offering in an alms box. When he turned around to come back, he found that Mary had left the bench. She had crossed the court and was standing near the door of one of the Council Chambers, where the scribes and doctors gathered together to discuss matters of the Law. She motioned him to come to her.

"Joseph," she said breathlessly, "that is Jesus' voice!" Her whole bearing had changed — she was young again.

Yes, it was the sweet young voice of Jesus, speaking quietly and clearly. Joseph and Mary listened, but they could not distinguish the words. Then the young voice stopped and older voices answered. Then came the boyish voice again.

They moved forward but the doorway was crowded — others too were trying to see. Presently someone in front of them moved and they saw Jesus, standing there unafraid, surrounded by a group

of solemn, bearded men. The men were asking and answering
questions and exclaiming to each other over the things that he
said. "Listen to the little doctor!" "Where did he learn these
things!" "The little rabbi certainly knows his points of Law!"

As Mary and Joseph listened, they were amazed too, for this
was a new Jesus. This wasn't the little boy they had lost three
days before. . . .

"Has his mission begun?" Mary asked herself. But just then
someone else moved away from in front of them, and Jesus saw
them. He turned, smiled, hesitated, and came toward them.

Suddenly the tears which Mary had held back so long rushed
into her eyes. "Son," she said in a low voice, "why have you done
this to us? Your father and I have sought you sorrowing."

Jesus turned troubled eyes upon her. "How is it you have
sought me?" he asked, surprised. "Did you not know I must be
about my Father's business?"

Mary's heart tightened. Had his time come to leave her? *This
Child shall be for the rise and fall of many*, she thought, remembering Simeon's words. If the time had come, she was ready. She
had long ago said to God, "Be it done unto me according to
Thy word."

But having spoken, Jesus turned and walked with them out of
the Council Chamber, quietly and simply, like the Jesus they had
always known. He was ready to go back with them to Nazareth.
The time had not yet come. . . .

Chapter VII

JESUS IS BAPTIZED BY JOHN

ICE fresh fish, lady — caught last night. Take some home for the Sabbath meal."

Mary paused by the fish stall, her basket on her arm. "You say it was caught last night?" She smiled at him kindly.

"Yes, lady. My boy goes down twice a week. There's an old fellow in Bethsaida I get it from. By the way, his sons have taken a fancy to that fellow John who's been making such a stir. He's come out of the desert and is preaching and baptizing down by the Jordan. Did you ever hear of him, lady?"

Mary smiled and nodded, but her heart tightened. So John had come out of the desert! John, the son of Zachary and Elizabeth! He had been leading a life of prayer and penance in the desert over beyond the Jordan since he was little more than a boy. "Yes, I've heard of him," she said.

"How many fish, please, lady?"

"May I have two, please, medium size?" Her thoughts were far away in Ain-Karim, on the words of Zachary the day little John received his name:

And thou, child, shalt be called the prophet of the Most High, and thou shalt go before the face of the Lord to prepare his ways. . . .

"I'll pick you out two nice ones, lady." He handled the shiny fish with practiced hands and selected two. "Do you want them in your basket?"

Mary took them and paid for them. "Thank you," she said. "The blessing of God be on you," but she was not thinking of the fish. She was thinking that if John's mission had begun, the time could not be far off for Jesus to begin his own mission. For John was to prepare his ways. . . .

Absorbed in her thoughts, she moved away from the fish stall.

"Lettuce, lady, fresh-picked. Take some home for the Sabbath meal."

"No, thank you," Mary said. "The blessing of God go with you." She moved on through the market place.

"Who's that?" asked the woman to the seller of onions in the next stall. She was a newcomer in Nazareth. "She's kind, sure enough — and pretty too."

"That's the widow of Joseph the carpenter. My father always said he was the best carpenter in Galilee, but her son Jesus is even better. No one knows all the kind things he does — making things and mending things for the poor without charge. He'd give away the clothes on his back if you asked him, and his mother's the same way. She sits up all night with the sick. She's young to be the mother of a man of thirty. . . ."

Mary crossed the market square and turned into the street of the carpenters. Jesus was working in the doorway of his shop, putting the finishing touches on a small oak chest. He straightened up and smiled with pleasure when he saw her. "Mother," he said, "that basket is too heavy. If you will wait a minute I'll walk home with you and carry it." He took the basket from her and brought her a stool to sit on. Then he went back to his work, but he looked up now and then and smiled.

She sat a moment in silence, watching him rub down the wood. His hands were strong and sure in their movements, but they could be gentle too. She remembered how tenderly those hands had taken care of Joseph — as tenderly as a woman.

"Jesus," she said presently, watching him closely, "your cousin John has come out of the desert and is preaching down by the Jordan."

He straightened up and was silent a moment.

"Yes, I know," he said softly. He did not need to say more — she understood. She watched him in silence as he polished the wood. He did not speak again until he had finished. Then he straightened up and said, "Mother, my time has almost come."

"Yes, I know, Jesus."

He took off his apron and hung it on the nail where Joseph always hung his apron at the end of the day. Everything in the shop spoke of Joseph; nothing was changed.

Jesus wrapped his cloak about him and took the basket. "I'm ready," he said smiling. It was early to be leaving; the sun was still high. The horn that announced the Sabbath Rest would not be sounding for some time. That was good — they would have a little time together. They were not alone very much any more. Since Joseph died, Mary of Cleophas, the widow of Joseph's brother, had been with them much of the time with her sons. But they were spending some days in Capharnaum. It would be good to be alone.

Jesus sat and talked to Mary as she prepared the food for the Sabbath. It was ready on the stove, just as it should be, when the first horn sounded for the Sabbath Rest. When the third horn sounded, she lit the Sabbath Lamp. Then they stood to pray together before supper:

> Blessed art thou, O Lord, our God . . .
> who bringeth forth bread from the earth. . . .

That evening they talked late of John, and of Jesus and his mission. They did not often speak of these things, but they were never far from their thoughts.

Nothing was different, for a while after that, about the way Jesus spent his days. But Mary noticed he was no longer taking any new orders. There was a wedding chest to finish for a bride in Cana, a plow for old Ruben, a carved table for the Ruler of the

Synagogue, window and door frames for a new house being built. These kept him busy from morning till night, but he would take no new requests.

"I wonder what has struck Jesus the carpenter," people began to say. "Do you think he's planning to leave town?" Then they would sigh, for there were not many carpenters like him any more.

Mary noticed too that more and more he was going up onto the hill above the town to pray. Often he prayed there all night, but he would be at the shop the next morning as usual, carving the chest for the bride of Cana, planing the boards for the Rabbi's table.

"I finished the chest today," he said one night to Mary as they were standing together in the doorway, watching the sun go down behind the hill. A few days later he said, "I've finished the Rabbi's table." Mary knew what this meant . . . the time was getting very close. Any day, now, he would be coming home and saying, "Tomorrow I'll be leaving you, Mother. My time has come."

Finally the day came. Mary was sitting by her loom in the gathering dusk with her shuttle in her lap. She had just finished one of those seamless garments which the women of Nazareth weave for their men. Jesus would need a new cloak when he started on his mission. It was ready to cut from the loom.

Her mind wandered over the past as she sat there. She thought of the tiny Jesus she had brought out of the desert, of the tall boy of twelve she had lost in the Temple, of Jesus and Joseph working together. She thought of the day Joseph had said to him, "Son, this is the way you prepare the lamb for the Passover Supper. You bind the legs so. No bone may be broken." It was the very next year that Joseph had begun to fail. She could still see him as clearly as though it was only yesterday, sitting in the shade of the lemon tree, waiting for Jesus to come home from work. "How did it go today?" he would ask Jesus wistfully. "Did you finish old Asahel's plow?" Then Jesus would tell him each thing he had done. The next winter, Joseph died and the old life together was over. And so the years had passed, and each year she wondered,

"When will he leave? When will his mission begin?" But he did not say and she did not ask — they were waiting for it to be God's will. But now the time had come — the time for which they both had prayed and waited — and the separation was going to be hard. . . .

Jesus was late in coming home that night, and when he pushed open the door, she could see by his face he had been praying. He sat down beside her and was silent a moment. Then he said very gently: "Mother, I'm leaving tomorrow for the River Jordan to be baptized by John." He watched her intently as he spoke. She trembled ever so slightly. Then she turned to him and smiled.

He did not need to tell her he would not be back again to stay — not in the old way. She knew without being told. She had been preparing for this day for thirty years.

*   *   *

The man called John the Baptist stood on the riverbank, surrounded by a small group of listeners. He had been baptizing, and the water still gleamed on his bronzed skin. It ran in little rivulets from his rough camel's-hair tunic. He stood, scarcely noticing it, intent on the men around him.

The crowd had dispersed, splashing through the shallow water of the ford and scrambling up the other bank to the Bethany road. There were Pharisees in fringed mantles, merchants riding donkeys with bulging saddlebags, poor men in rough clothes, soldiers in the livery of Herod. Some looked very serious; some were even crying — big, bearded men with tears on their sunburnt faces. But the Pharisees were angry — very angry. For John had seen through their pretenses to holiness, and he had not minced his words. He had called them vipers. "Repent," he warned them, "for the Kingdom of Heaven is at hand."

"Just think, he called us vipers!" they said to one another as they made their way through the tangle of vines along the Jordan River. "Vipers!" The veins stood out in anger on their foreheads.

But now they were gone, and John was left with the people who really cared, the people who were really sorry for their sins. They were plain, simple people, fishermen, vine dressers, soldiers — even a few publicans, whom everyone despised because they were so often dishonest in collecting the taxes. But John did not despise them; they too belonged in the Kingdom of Heaven if they truly repented.

"Master, what shall we do?" they asked him.

His stern face softened. "Exact no more than the taxes," he said simply. And to the soldiers: "Molest no one, make no false accusations, and be content with your pay." But to those who were very much in earnest he said: "If you have two cloaks, give one to the man who has none."

He looked from one to another, letting his eyes rest on each one. He knew they were dear to God. Then he stopped speaking and looked out over the broad basin of the Jordan to the road on the other side. It was a crooked road, dipping and climbing, twisting and turning. It was not an important road and no one had bothered to pull out the stumps and boulders that lay in its way. The road went around them instead.

As John looked at that road, he thought of his work of preparing for the Messias. It was the work of making straight a road, a road that ran twisting and curving through men's souls. The stumps and boulders were their sins. He must make that road straight. He must make it straight for the Messias, the Redeemer, whom he had never seen, but who was coming soon. Sometimes he grew weary of saying the same things over and over to men who were evil and obstinate and angry. But when he thought of the Messias, he shook off his weariness, tightened his leather belt, and began again: *Repent, for the Kingdom of Heaven is at hand.* . . .

He stood now, resting his eyes on the silvery water, preparing to speak again. He looked up and saw someone coming toward him, making his way quickly and quietly through the group. He was a man of about John's own age, supple and straight, dressed in the seamless cloak of a Galilean. John gazed for a moment into the face of the stranger. It was a wonderful face. As John looked at the man he felt his heart beat faster. The man's eyes seemed to pierce to his very soul.

The man started to speak; he was asking to be baptized. But John had a strange, clear sense that here was a man who had never sinned. How could he baptize such a man, he who was so unworthy? He drew back quickly.

"I ought to be baptized by you," he said, "and do you come to me?"

"Let it be so for the present," the stranger answered quietly. And so John led him down into the water and baptized him. Then they came out together onto the riverbank. The man stood silent, praying. *Can it be he?* John was wondering. *Can this be the Messias?* But there was no sign. God had told him there would be a sign — he should see a dove resting on his shoulders. . . .

Suddenly, as they stood there, the sky opened. A dove flew down and hovered about the stranger. It alighted on his shoulder. A voice from heaven cried out:

This is my beloved Son, in whom I am well pleased. . . .

John stepped back trembling. At last the moment had come, the moment for which he had been preparing and praying all these years. He did not know the name of the man before him. He did not know he was Jesus of Nazareth, Son of Mary. But he knew he was the Promised One, the Son of God.

For a time he was too moved to speak. Indeed, he could hardly see. When he looked again at Jesus, the dove was gone, but Jesus was still praying.

The little group of bystanders was staring about in confusion at the sky, at Jesus, at John.

"Did you hear something, neighbor? Did you hear a voice?"

"What do you think it was?"

"And the sky — did you see how it seemed to open?"

John and Jesus stood facing each other, and John thought, with a sudden rush of joy: "My work is almost over. I must decrease and he must increase." Jesus, looking at him, loved him, and thought: "There is no man born of woman who is greater than John the Baptist."

Chapter VIII

JESUS GOES TO A WEDDING

ARY stepped to the doorway for a breath of air. It was good to get away for a moment from the bustle and stir. The bride and bridesmaids were ready, and the women were crowding around the little bride.

"Ah, my pretty, the bridegroom wins a prize this time!"

"Hold up your head, my darling. The veil hangs better so."

"The rings and bracelets are lovely! The blessing of God be on you."

The bride's mother stood beaming and talking excitedly: "Ah, my baby, my darling! It's a proud day when a mother sees her daughter led to the house of the bridegroom!"

Mary smiled to herself as she listened. She had come to Cana early to help with the preparations for the wedding. She had filled the lamps for the bridesmaids. She had helped arrange the bridal crown. She had been everywhere at once, doing whatever was needed. "Mary, can you help arrange this veil?" "Mary, can you fasten this bracelet?" It was a wonderful thing to see a man and woman coming together to become man and wife. A new home was starting, a new house in Israel where God would be praised. Yes, it was a wonderful thing. She thought of the beautiful words of the marriage blessing:

Blessed be Thou, O Lord our God, the creator of man . . .
Make this couple to rejoice with joy. . . .

Turning from the merry bustle inside, she peered down the street
in the deepening dusk. The men were gathered outside the bridegroom's house, waiting for it to be dark enough to light the
torches for the procession. Had Jesus come? Was he among them?
Perhaps he had not got the message. . . .

It was more than six weeks since he had left for the Jordan to
be baptized. The day after his baptism, he had disappeared. "He's
been gone a long time," Mary of Cleophas said one day. "It's strange
he has sent no word." But Mary was not surprised. She knew
what he would want to do before he began his mission. He would
want to go off somewhere and pray. She knew, for she had been
praying too. Then after the long silence she had received word
that he was back again at the Jordan. Men were beginning to
follow him — some of John's disciples. There were two fishermen
from Bethsaida called Simon and Andrew, a man named Philip
from Capharnaum, Nathanael from Cana. Nathanael would know
about the wedding. She hoped Jesus would come. . . .

She watched the torches take light one by one in the crowd
outside the bridegroom's house. Then the music began, the flutes
and the tambourines. Soon the procession would be starting up
the street to the house of the bride. She stepped back into the
house. "They are coming," she said softly to the bride. "The Lord
bless you, my dear."

Suddenly the chatter ceased. "Mary says they are coming."

The mother kissed the little bride once more and then lowered
her long bridal veil. It would never do for the bridegroom to see
her face until she had crossed the threshold of his house!

They formed in line and waited — the bride, the bridesmaids,
her family, her friends. The silence was tense and breathless. You
could hear people breathing. Someone coughed. A baby whimpered.
"Hush, my darling. Hush. Listen to the music. It's coming closer."
Nearer and nearer came the flutes and tambourines. The torches
threw long shadows across the walls from the latticed windows.

The bridesmaids' lamps trembled in their hands. There it was now! There was the bridegroom's cry!

Come out for the bridegroom calleth for thee. . . .

The cry was followed by shouts and laughter from the crowd outside. The bride and her bridesmaids passed through the doorway. There was a moment of joyous confusion as the two groups mingled. Then the procession formed again and started down the street toward the bridegroom's house in the flickering torchlight. As the lights flared up, Mary searched the crowd for a familiar face. She did not find it. Jesus had not come. . . .

Into the groom's house went the bride and groom. In came all the people with the flutes and tambourines playing. Then there was silence.

Blessed be Thou, O Lord Our God. . . .
Blessed art thou who makest the bride and bridegroom to rejoice. . . .

It was a long blessing, a beautiful blessing. The bride's hand shook a little as she was led by the bridegroom to their place under the bridal canopy. Her mother stepped forward to kiss her. "Lift up your veil, my darling!" She lifted it up with trembling hands, smiling and blushing. The guests rushed forward to greet them. They were man and wife!

Such a bustle and stir as there was! But at last the guests were all seated and the wedding-feast began. Mary was seated near the door with the guests of the bride. She was glad, for she had not yet given up hope that Jesus might come. People kept asking her about him.

"Is Jesus coming, Mary? What's this we hear about his going away? It's not for long, I hope."

The feast was well under way, and Mary had almost decided that he was not coming, when there was a knock at the door. She looked up and saw him in the doorway with his new companions. He was talking to the Master of the Feast, introducing them one by one: "This is Simon from Bethsaida, but we call

him Peter. This is Andrew, his brother. This is Philip — and James —
and John. You know Nathanael. . . ." There were greetings, and
gay, friendly laughter. Jesus had an understanding way.

"He seems thinner and older," Mary thought as she watched
him. "He has been fasting." But his face was tanned and his
voice had its same clear ring. His new companions were big,
bronzed, simple men. So that was the kind he had chosen! He
would ask God first in prayer. . . .

People looked up from their places when he came into the
room to greet the host. So Jesus had come!

"He's been away, you know. We've heard he's given up his
carpenter's shop, but we don't know whether it's true. These men
are friends of his. . . ."

"Those two from Bethsaida — aren't they the sons of Zebedee?
He's a mighty fine fellow, old Zebedee!"

After Jesus had greeted the bride and groom, he came and sat
down with his companions near where Mary was sitting. She
could not hear what they said over the din of voices and clattering
dishes, but she saw that they kept plying him with questions so that
he could hardly eat. He answered them earnestly, but now and then
he looked over at her and smiled. It was a quick, secret smile which
seemed to say: "We are doing this together, you and I. We understand. We do not need to speak to share what we do." Then he
turned back again to answer some question of Andrew or Nathanael
or Simon Peter. He looked up as the waiters came by with more fish
or wine. "No thank you, no more," he said, but he smiled at them
in a way that made them feel: "We too are his friends."

The banquet was going well, to judge by the talk and laughter.
Mary from her corner with the other women, watched the waiters
as they moved about with the meat, the bread, the fruit, the
wine. "The steward has provided well," she thought, and she was
glad, for the host's sake. She turned again to look at Jesus. He
was still speaking earnestly to his little group.

"Jesus looks well," someone said to her from across the table.
She answered in her usual kindly way, but her thoughts were on

those sunburnt faces that were leaning toward Jesus. They were catching fire, those faces. They were eager and very much in earnest. She was glad.

Suddenly her attention was attracted by one of the waiters. He was looking about with concern and motioning to another waiter. He pointed to his wine jar and the other shook his head. Mary understood his gestures. The wine had given out.

She was never quite sure afterward what led her to speak to Jesus, or what she expected him to do. All she could remember was that she had a sudden impulse to go and speak to him. Slipping quietly over, she said in a low voice, "Jesus, they have no wine."

He looked at her slowly, thoughtfully. She had a queer sense that he was looking less at her than beyond her, and when he answered, he spoke in a strange, formal way, as though he were not speaking to his mother.

"Woman, what would you have me do? My hour is not yet come."

Mary searched his face, puzzled at his words. As she watched him, his expression changed. A look of intense wonder crossed his face. Something caught fire within her, and she knew what she must do. She turned and beckoned to the waiter. "Do whatever he tells you," she said quietly, motioning with her hand toward Jesus.

The look of wonder had faded, and Jesus was regarding her fixedly. When the waiter came over, he pointed to the six stone water jars that stood near the door.

"Fill them with water to the brim," he said quietly.

The waiter looked about, bewildered, and then did as he was bidden. By now several of the guests had noticed and were watching him. He poured in water, pitcher after pitcher, until the jars were filled. Then he came back to Jesus.

"Draw some now and take it to the Master of the Feast."

The startled waiter did as he was told. Suddenly there was an uproar, for out of the jar there came, not water — but wine. It smelled like wine; it looked like wine; it tasted like wine. There was no room for doubt.

The waiter's hand shook as he carried it to the Master of the Feast. The Master, who had not been close enough to see, tasted it and then took it to the host. "How is this?" he said. "Everyman at first sets out the best wine, and when men have well drunk, sets out that which is worse. But you have kept the good wine till now!"

But by now the uproar had spread from table to table until it reached the host. The story was incredible but true. "We saw it with our own eyes," people said to one another. "Jesus of Nazareth turned water into wine!"

"Turned water into wine? What are you saying, man! That cannot be!"

"But it is true. We saw it! Try it and see if you have ever tasted better wine!"

"How did he do it?"

"He had the man fill the water jars with water, but what they drew was not water but wine!"

On every side, tongues were buzzing with it, and people were jumping up and rushing over to see the wonderful jars.

Yes, truly they were filled with wine, truly!

The companions of Jesus stood in a little group, apart from the rest. They did not rush over to see the jars. They did not talk noisily to one another. They stood silent, in awe at what had happened. To them, it was more than just a strange occurrence. It was a sign from God. They had not been mistaken in following this Jesus, this man whom John had pointed out to them. The Voice they had heard that day beside the Jordan had truly come from heaven. . . .

This is my beloved Son, in whom I am well pleased. . . .

The tears came to their eyes. God had been very good. . . .

Mary slipped out for a moment into the darkness to quiet the beating of her heart. She had never doubted the message of the angel, the prophecies of Simeon and Anna, the wonderful witness of Elizabeth. Through all the thirty years she had not doubted. But now at last, in response to her words, she had seen Jesus being more than man. Today she had see him being the Son of God.

Chapter IX

NICODEMUS COMES TO JESUS
BY NIGHT

HE Pharisee Nicodemus paced back and forth in the courtyard of his house. The lamps in the great bronze lampstands were casting long, wavering shadows, and he could hear hushed movements through the house. His guests had retired, and now his servants were locking doors and extinguishing lamps. Soon they too would be going to their quarters. What was he doing, pacing up and down like this? What had happened to him, Nicodemus — man of wealth, Pharisee, and honored member of the Sanhedrin? Why could he not get this man Jesus out of his mind? He had no business to be bothering his thoughts about a wonder-worker from Nazareth, a carpenter with a Galilean accent!

He should be indignant, like the other Pharisees after the scene that morning in the Temple. And yet, the worst of it was — the Galilean had been right. The sellers of the sacrificial animals and the money-changers were a disgrace. They were making the Temple courts a den of thieves, just as the carpenter had said. But why did he have to bring the Priests and Pharisees all down about his ears like a nest of hornets? How could he ever hope to win them over? Nicodemus could not help smiling a little as he remembered that scene. He was not always in sympathy with some of his fellow

Pharisees, though he would never let them know it. They were a solemn-faced, self-righteous lot.

He stopped a moment in his pacing. Was *he* solemn-faced and self-righteous too? He did not like that thought. He started pacing again.

This Jesus, who was already getting well known for his miracles, had come up with his followers to the Temple for the Passover sacrifices. He had become suddenly angered at all the buying and selling that was going on in the Temple Esplanade. Men said he had made a whip of cords and had driven out the venders — men and beasts together. Such a bellowing and bleating as there had been! He had overturned the tables of the money-changers, but he had not let loose the cages of doves. "Take these out," he had said to the venders of doves, but that was all. They were poor, and this Jesus, it seemed, was a friend of the poor. "That's because he is poor himself, I guess," Nicodemus thought.

They had heard the uproar clear inside the Temple in the Council Chamber and had rushed out, he and the other members of the Sanhedrin. "It's that Galilean, Jesus," the guards had said as the priests rushed out to inquire. Sure enough, there he was, standing in the midst of the overturned tables with his companions around him, looking, not angry, but very, very sad.

If he had only not given the Pharisees and the Chief Priests that answer about rebuilding the Temple!

"Give us a sign to show by what authority you do this thing," the Priests had commanded him, remembering his reputation for miracles.

He had looked at them very quietly and had answered: "Destroy this Temple, and in three days I will rebuild it." Three days to rebuild the Temple? It had taken forty-six years to build it! That was an insane answer — unless perhaps it was a riddle. Men said he sometimes talked to them in riddles. This man with the deep, quiet eyes did not look insane.

It was the eyes that Nicodemus could not forget as he paced up and down in his house. They had turned and gazed full at him as he stood with the other Pharisees in the dismantled courtyard. They had looked right into his soul, those eyes. They seemed to be pleading for something. . . .

What nonsense it was to be thinking of these things! And yet the man, the rabbi, had preached wonderful things about a Kingdom of Heaven. He had promised to those who would follow him the gift of Eternal Life. . . .

Nicodemus paused again. Why should he not go and see this man? What harm could come of it? He would go by night. None of the other Pharisees would know. He could go this very night! It was not too late. . . .

He started pacing again. Was he losing his mind, he, Nicodemus, Pharisee and most honored member of the Sanhedrin? But those eyes — there were no eyes like them. He would go.

He motioned to a servant who had not yet retired. "Ahab, a lantern."

"Yes, sir."

"And my cloak."

"Yes, sir."

"And Ahab, do not say I have gone out."

"No, sir."

The man wrapped the cloak about his shoulders, handed him the lantern, and pulled back the bolts of the great door. Slowly it swung upon its hinges. Nicodemus slipped out into the night.

*   *   *

Jesus sat late with his disciples, that first night in Jerusalem, after their supper was over. He had been speaking to them of many things, but now he had lapsed into silence. He was either thinking or praying — they could not tell which. They were beginning to come to the conclusion that all his thoughts were prayers.

Simon, called Peter, shifted his position a little. He longed to ask Jesus what he had meant that morning about rebuilding the Temple in three days; but there was something in the Master's look that stopped him. Instead, he ran his fingers back and forth along the edge of the table. He was thinking about that first day by the River Jordan when Jesus had asked to be baptized by John. He was thinking of the hours they had spent with Jesus in the little hut down by the river after Jesus came back from his forty days in the desert. He thought too of the miracle in Cana, the first that Jesus had worked. There had been other miracles since then. People had brought their sick to be healed, their babies to be blessed. He was very gentle with them — as gentle as a woman. It was a surprisingly different Jesus who had driven the venders and money-changers out of the Temple that morning. Simon-Peter had never seen him that way before. But the anger was no ordinary anger. There was love in it — love for that beautiful, holy place. Jesus had called it his Father's house.

Simon-Peter shifted his position again, stiff from sitting all evening. He was used to an outdoor life. Andrew, near him, was mending his sandal, and John had fallen asleep on a bench by the door. John was young and fell asleep easily, but he loved the Master very much. He would be sorry when he discovered he had slept. . . .

Suddenly there was a knock at the door. John sat up with a jerk and opened his eyes. "Shall I answer it, Master?" he asked. Jesus nodded. When he opened the heavy oak door, he gave a start of surprise at the figure that greeted him. Under the stranger's rich, dark cloak, he could see the long, fringed mantle of a Pharisee. A Pharisee here, at this hour, in this part of town!

"Is the Rabbi here?" the stranger asked, flashing his lantern in John's startled eyes. John blinked and looked at Jesus. Again Jesus nodded.

"Yes, the Master is here."

Nicodemus stepped inside. So this was the place where the wonder-worker was staying! A table, three or four benches, a hard earthen floor. It was a poor sort of room. Nicodemus lifted the ends of his mantle as he stepped inside. But when he saw the Master, nothing else mattered. For those eyes were looking at him, those wonderful, kind eyes, with their loving, searching look.

Jesus showed no sign of surprise. He came forward and greeted his guest as though it was the most natural thing in the world to be entertaining one of the richest Pharisees in Jerusalem in the dead of night in his borrowed lodgings. Nicodemus sat down on one of the rough benches, gathering his skirts about him.

"Rabbi," he said. "We know you come from God. No one could work the miracles you do if God were not with him." He paused a moment and cleared his throat, choosing his words.

Jesus regarded the angular, nervous face, measuring in his mind how far this man was ready to go. He did not wait for the visitor to frame his question.

"Amen, I say to you," he said quietly, "no one can see the Kingdom of God, unless he be born again."

The bearded face of the stranger twitched and grew more angular. The hands with their jeweled rings clutched hold of the table. There was sarcasm in his answer: "How can a man be born again when he is old?"

Jesus went on quietly, taking no notice of the tone of the question.

"Amen, I say to you: no man can enter the Kingdom of God unless he be born of water and the Holy Spirit. What is born of the flesh is flesh, and what is born of the spirit is spirit."

The smile had faded from the visitor's face now. Those kind eyes made him suddenly ashamed of his question. The Rabbi had taken no notice of its tone at all. He was treating him like a friend, a follower.

Jesus went on. "Wonder not that I say to you, 'You must be born again.' The Spirit breathes where it will; and you hear his voice, but you know not whence he comes or whither he goes. So is everyone that is born of the Spirit."

Nicodemus sat clutching the edge of the table, looking hard at the Master's face, trying to find the meaning of those strange words. Simon-Peter and the other disciples were sitting up very straight now, listening. Every day Jesus gave them some new truth, but it seemed they could never hear enough.

Nicodemus answered again with a question, but this time there was no mockery in his voice. He was mystified, and he wanted to understand.

"How can this be done?"

Jesus looked at him closely. Here was a Pharisee, a ruler of the Synagogue, a teacher of the people, and he had no idea that God wanted to be worshiped in spirit, and that the Kingdom of God was a Kingdom of the Spirit. These Pharisees wanted a different kind of kingdom; they wanted a Messias who would bring them earthly power.

His voice was sad as he asked: "Are you a master in Israel, and you do not know these things?" He did not wait for an answer. "If I have spoken to you of earthly things and you do not believe, how will you believe if I speak to you of heavenly things?"

He was silent a minute; then once again he started to speak, letting the words pour from him, wonderful words that set Peter to sitting on the edge of his seat and set young John to trembling.

No man hath ascended into heaven but he that descendeth from heaven, the Son of Man who is in heaven. And as Moses lifted up the serpent in the desert, so must the Son of Man be lifted up. That whosoever believeth in him may not perish, but may have life everlasting. For God so loved the world as to give his only-begotten Son, that whosoever believeth in him may not perish, but may have life everlasting.

All this he said and more, while Peter and John clutched the edge of the table, trying to hold onto those words, to remember them for all time. *The Son of Man must be lifted up . . . for God so loved the world. . . .*

They tried to hold onto words which they only half understood. It was often so with what he said. Sometimes he would explain when they asked; sometimes he only shook his head. The time had not yet come when they could understand. Some day they would know all things — some day when they were ready.

The look of bewilderment had deepened on the face of Nicodemus. The bewilderment had been followed by weariness. It was no use! He could not understand. This man was more than a wonder-worker! Was he a prophet? Why did he talk in riddles? And yet he would bear watching. There was something about him — an air of authority. But now he must go. He must go back home before anyone noticed his absence. His wife would be missing him and would inquire. You could never trust a woman to hold her tongue!

He stood up slowly and thanked the Rabbi for his words. "Very interesting," he said, rubbing his hands. "Very interesting." He picked up his lantern and gathered his cloak about him. But as he turned to go, he saw those eyes looking at him again. They were sad, disappointed eyes this time. Once more they searched his face. They followed him, in his thoughts, all the way home. And so did the Master's strange words: *Unless you be born again . . . For God so loved the world. . . .* They were wonderful words, even though one could not understand them. They set vague, strange desires to stirring in one's mind. Some day he would talk to this man again — some day. . . .

Jesus went to the door and looked after the retreating figure, whose quick, nervous steps echoed in the silent street. The city was quiet now, except for a dog here or there, barking. He was thinking of Nicodemus, and of how hard it was for the rich and powerful to believe in his kingdom. There was so much they would have to give up!

He turned and gazed for a moment at the little group gathered about the table in the flickering lamplight. He looked at them as though he were measuring each one, but lovingly, as a mother studies her children. How much had they understood? Not very much. But without understanding they had believed. That was why he loved them. He loved them for their generous trust.

He gave his quick, characteristic little nod, which they had learned to look for in the weeks they had been with him. Then, turning suddenly, he slipped out into the night.

They knew he had gone out to pray.

Chapter X

JESUS IS DRIVEN OUT OF NAZARETH

ARY climbed the steps of the Nazareth Synagogue, caught up in the crowd around her. Pharisees and merchants brushed shoulders with laborers from the vineyards, for it was the Sabbath and the hour for worship. People were talking more noisily than usual, for Jesus had come back to Nazareth. He had been seen mounting the steps of the Synagogue.

"Jesus is back. Did you see him?"

"No. How did he look?"

"Not very different. Thinner, perhaps. I wonder if the tales about him are true."

"You mean about turning the water into wine? And about driving the money-changers out of the Temple? My brother was at the wedding, and he swears it's true about the wine."

"They say the chief priests were madder than hornets over that scene in the Temple."

"Hush, isn't that his mother? She'll hear what you say."

Mary drew away, but others were speaking, wherever she turned.

"Isn't it wonderful about Jesus! Did you hear he's back? My cousin from Bethsaida knows two of his disciples. She says he has even healed the sick."

"Look, there's his mother. She must be very proud."
"Isn't it wonderful, Mary, to have Jesus back!"

Mary was glad when she reached the door and could slip inside
to a seat in the women's section. It was still early, and she sat for
a moment with her eyes shut, resting her mind from the noise and
bustle outside. Yes, Jesus had come back. He had stolen in, shortly
before the first horn sounded for the Sabbath rest, hot and tired.
He had sat down beside her for a moment in silence, after his first
greeting. Then he had said quietly: "John the Baptist is in prison.
He rebuked Herod." They were silent again, each knowing the
other's thoughts. Judea was no longer safe. That was why Jesus
had come back. It was too soon to run into needless danger. His
mission had only just begun. . . .

Mary opened her eyes and looked around the rapidly filling
Synagogue. There, in one of the first seats, sat Jesus. His weeks
away had gained that honor for him. But that was not what mattered. What counted was the number of souls he had stirred with
his message: "Repent for the Kingdom of Heaven is at hand. . . ."
"Unless a man be born again, he cannot see the Kingdom of God."
How many had he set on fire? That was what she was praying for
now. That was what really mattered. . . .

Jesus looked rested, wonderfully rested. She knew he had been
on the hill above the town, praying. That always rested him better
than sleep. . . .

She looked down again, preparing her thoughts for the morning
worship. In a minute the Ruler of the Synagogue would rise; he
would begin with the holy words. Her heart must be ready. She
sat with her eyes shut, praying. Presently a voice broke her thoughts.
"Hear, O Israel," came the high-pitched voice, intoning.

> The Lord our God is one Lord.
> Thou shalt love the Lord thy God
>   with thy whole heart
>   and with thy whole soul
>   and with thy whole strength.

And these words which I command thee
This day shall be in thy heart. . . .

Then came the Eighteen Benedictions. Mary sat very still, letting her mind rest on the beautiful words. She could never hear them often enough. Each day she had recited them, ever since she could remember. She had said them with old Anna in the Temple, with Joseph, with Jesus. They meant most of all when she said them with Jesus. He had shown her new meanings for the old words. The congregation recited them now together, but in her heart she was saying them with Jesus. . . .

Then there was a moment of silence. She did not look up, but she knew that the Synagogue attendant had gone to take the great scroll from its place and bring it to the Ruler of the Synagogue. Sometimes the Ruler read from it himself; sometimes he offered it to a distinguished visitor to read. It was a way of honoring a guest.

Mary could feel a restlessness around her. People were craning their necks to see: would the Ruler offer the Scriptures to Jesus? He had been ushered to one of the chief seats; he was already becoming known in Israel. But after all, he was only Jesus. He had not studied with any of the great teachers. What did he know about the Prophecies?

Yes, the Ruler had spoken to the attendant, and now he was taking the scroll to Jesus. Jesus stood up and opened the volume. He looked out over the congregation, and then he read in a loud, clear voice:

The Spirit of the Lord is upon me
Because he has anointed me;
To bring good news to the poor he has sent me,
to proclaim to the captives release,
and sight to the blind;
To set at liberty the oppressed,
to proclaim the acceptable year of the Lord,
and the day of recompense.

Closing the volume, he gave it back to the attendant and sat down. Mary, sitting quietly in the women's section, trembled ever so slightly as she listened. It was the first time she had heard Jesus speaking in public, but that was not why she trembled. It was at the words he had chosen to read. They were words which foretold his mission as Messias. She sat very still, praying . . .

The eyes of all were on him, now, waiting for him to speak. He paused a moment, and then he called out clearly:

Today, this Scripture has been fulfilled in your hearing.

For a moment there was silence. Then a confused murmur started, which grew more and more angry. Some, to be sure, marveled at his words. They were full of wonder and admiration. But others scoffed and mocked him. "Is not this Joseph's son? Isn't this Jesus the carpenter?"

Jesus stood up and stretched out his hand to quiet the crowd. "You will surely quote me this proverb," he said quietly, " 'Physician, cure thyself.' You will say 'whatever things we have heard of as done in Capharnaum, do here also in your own country.' Amen I say to you, no prophet is acceptable in his own country."

The murmur began again, louder this time and angrier. So — he was telling them it was *their* fault if he did not work miracles among them! He *was* pretending to be the Messias, and it was *their* fault if they did not believe! They would show him how to speak in his own town! They would put him in his proper place! They rose to their feet and started toward him. Those nearest him laid rough hands on him and pushed him toward the door. "Get the blasphemer out! Do away with him!" In a moment the whole place was a seething, shoving, shouting mob. "Get the blasphemer out of here!"

They pushed and shoved him out of the Synagogue, and then the crowd waited a moment. This was the Sabbath, and the hour of worship. One or two started to go back in. Then someone began shouting: "Get him out of the town! Get the blasphemer out of here! Away with him! Take him to the top of the hill. Over the cliff with the blasphemer! He is worthy to die!"

Others took up the cry: "Over the cliff with him!" They pulled and shoved him along, through the market place, up the narrow streets, past the well, on up to the top of the hill. "Over the cliff with him! Let him die for his words!"

"Hear, O God, my supplication. Be attentive to my prayer," prayed Mary, in the words of the Shepherd-King David. She was forced along by the pressure of the crowd, whether she willed it or no.

"Come, Mary, come," Mary of Cleophas urged, taking her arm. "Here is a chance to get away. You can't help him by being there. It will only make it harder for you if you follow them. You can slip through here."

But Mary only shook her head. Her place was with Jesus, whatever they might do to him. She pulled her cloak tighter around her and allowed herself to be carried along by the crowd. "Hear, O God, my prayer," she prayed. "Despise not my supplication."

The mob had reached the top of the hill, now, and were elbowing and shoving, pushing Jesus closer and closer to the cliff. "Over the cliff with him! Over the cliff with the carpenter who calls himself the Messias!"

Mary could not see Jesus. She could only see the maddened crowd. But only a short time before, these people had been her friends! They had been the friends and neighbors of Jesus! He had made the merchant his counter, the cobbler his workbench, the farmer his plow. He had bought shoes from them, corn from them. And when they were poor he had given the last coins in his purse to them. . . .

"Over the cliff with him!" they were shouting.

"Hear, O God, my supplication," prayed Mary.

Suddenly there was a shout of anger — a disappointed frenzied shout.

"Look out, there! Where did he go! He's given us the slip! The carpenter has got away! Which way did he go? Did anyone see?"

Mary stepped back into the shelter of a tree, now that the danger was over. She was white and shaken, but Jesus was safe. God had been very good — he had worked what was surely a miracle. She prayed, as she leaned a moment against the tree, catching her breath, but this time it was a prayer of thanksgiving:

Give glory to the Lord for he is good;
for his mercy endureth forever. . . .

"Come, Mary. We must get out of here before they see us. They are very angry that Jesus got away." Mary of Cleophas touched her on the arm anxiously. "Come — some of them will recognize you."

Mary nodded, and together, they slipped away from the crowd and took a narrow trail that led down steeply to their house. It was a short cut that not many would know. They were already safe in the house when the men and women of Nazareth turned in their tracks and started back down the way they had come. Their excitement was beginning to cool. Some of them were a little ashamed, a little relieved that Jesus had escaped from their hands. Gradually they would forget their anger. Once more he would come to preach to them — only once. They would not harm him a second time, but they would scoff at him. Yes, it was true: "A prophet is not without honor except in his own country."

Chapter XI

PETER, ANDREW, JAMES, AND JOHN BECOME FISHERS OF MEN

IMON PETER braced himself in his boat and started to pull on the rope. Then he relaxed his hold, for the net was empty. He pulled it up, slimy and dripping, and dropped it into the boat. Andrew let go of his oars and wiped his face. They had been out all night, working up and down the shore between Capharnaum and Bethsaida, and had caught nothing. James and John, who had kept close to them in their father Zebedee's boat, had had no more success. Four fishermen had only a little seaweed trailing from their nets to show for their night's work.

Andrew regarded his brother's tired face, and swung the boat around, heading toward shore with strong, even strokes. He could hear the dip of John's oars just behind him. It was no use to try further; they might better go home and sleep. The next night they might have more success. Soon they were in shallow water and the two boats ran up the beach with a grating sound. In a moment, they were pulled up out of the water and the wet nets lay on the beach. Like good fishermen, the men spread them out to dry and started picking out the seaweed.

The sun was well above the hills now, and the lake lay like a mirror, harp-shaped in a circle of hills. They were a short distance below Capharnaum, and they could hear men calling to each other as they unloaded oil and fish at the Capharnaum wharf. Farther up the lake toward Tiberias, sails were shining white and a Roman galley was passing. The day's work had begun on the shores of Lake Genesareth.

The four had much to think about as they leaned over their nets in the early morning light. Fishing was not very important to them any longer, after their wonderful weeks with Jesus. They had come back to it rather halfheartedly, hoping each day to see Jesus, to hear him once more, to be a part of the crowd as he preached or healed the sick. They would never forget their days with him in Jerusalem and their journey back to Galilee together. He had stopped for several days in each town they came to, teaching and healing the sick, but he had let them baptize. They had done it with their big fishermen's hands, half frightened to be doing it. Yes, those were wonderful weeks. And then, just as everything was progressing so well, the message had come about John the Baptist. "We must go back to Galilee," Jesus had said very quietly, but his face was sad. And so they had returned and had scattered to their homes, but Jesus was still preaching. When he preached in or near Capharnaum, they left their boats turned over on the beach and went to hear him. His message was still the same: *Repent for the Kingdom of Heaven is at hand.* . . .

With these memories to occupy them as they cleaned and mended their nets, they paid small attention to the voices that drifted toward them over the beach. But gradually they grew louder — the voices of many people talking and laughing. Looking up, they saw a crowd coming slowly toward them along the edge of the lake. The four fishermen stood a moment, watching; then they dropped their nets and started along the beach toward the voices. Jesus was coming toward them, surrounded as usual by an eager, noisy multitude.

The crowd dropped back, and Jesus came forward to meet them. Looking first at them and then at their empty nets, he read at a glance the record of their fruitless night and smiled. "Come with

me and I will make you fishers of men," he said to Peter and
Andrew, who were nearer to him. Then he went on to James and
John and repeated: "Come with me and I will make you fishers
of men." He was not smiling now; he was serious; he meant just
what he said. His words set their hearts to pounding. Jesus, the
Master, wanted them. Their time of helping him was not over;
they were going to have a share in founding his kingdom. . . .

But the people had come up now to Jesus and were pressing
close around him. They wanted him to speak. Jesus looked out over
the pushing jostling crowd, and then at Peter's boat. "Push it out
a little way," he said to Peter. Peter turned it over and shoved it
down into the water.

The crowd watched with puzzled eyes. Was the Master going
to leave without speaking to them? "Master, don't go," they pleaded.
"Stay and tell us more about your kingdom."

Jesus smiled and nodded, but he climbed into the boat. Peter
gave it a push that sent it out into the shallow water; then he
swung it around and steadied it with his oars. The watching
crowd understood and smiled. The Master was going to speak to
them from the boat! He stood in the sun, with the water lapping
against the sides of the boat, talking to them as he had never talked
before. The sun climbed higher and beat down hotter and hotter,
but the crowd went on listening without noticing. The morning
was far advanced when he finally stopped speaking and they left
him and went about their business. "Surely this Jesus is a prophet,"
they said to one another, as they walked slowly along the beach
toward Capharnaum. "He speaks with authority and not like the
scribes and Pharisees." It was the chief talk that day on the wharves
and in the market place. "Did you hear Jesus of Nazareth this
morning? He spoke from Simon's boat."

When the crowd had gone, Peter ran the boat up on the beach
and Jesus climbed out. Jesus looked at Peter and then at the empty
nets. "Put them into the boat," he said to Peter. "Push out into
the deep. Now cast your nets for the fish." Peter flushed ever
so slightly.

"Master, we have worked all night without taking anything, but at your word I will cast the net."

Jesus stood on the shore, watching, as they dropped the big net over the side of the boat. It had hardly splashed into the water when the ropes tightened suddenly, the net bursting with fish. Peter and Andrew tugged at the ropes in amazement, and it was all they could do to raise the net. When they finally pulled it in, it almost capsized the boat, and they could scarcely bring their sinking craft to shore. When at last they landed it, Peter rushed trembling to Jesus and fell on his knees before him.

"Depart from me, O Lord," he said, still trembling, "for I am a sinful man."

Jesus smiled. "Be not afraid," he said. "Hereafter you shall be fishers of men."

Peter knelt a moment in front of Jesus. Then he rose slowly to his feet and went back to the boat. He and Andrew pulled it up once more onto the shore and dragged out the heavy net. Then, without looking back, the four men started with Jesus toward the town. Their old life was over; their new life had begun, their life as fishers of men.

*   *   *

On the evening of the next Sabbath, Peter leaned for a moment against the wall of his house, trying to collect his thoughts. Was he the same Peter he had been that morning? Was this the same house? How could everything change so completely? It was past midnight and the crowds kept coming. It seemed as though everyone in Capharnaum had been in his house that day. They kept crowding in as the fish had crowded into his net, the morning when Jesus called him.

It all began with his wife's mother, who was sick with a fever. "Simon, bring home the Master," his wife had pleaded, as he had started out that morning for the synagogue. "He healed an officer's son the other day in Cana. Ask him to heal her." And so, Peter had brought the Master back with him from the synagogue. The sick woman had grown worse during the morning, and the neighbors were crowding around her, wringing their hands. "She has the look of death on her," one of them was saying. "That is the way my mother looked the day before she died."

Jesus had gone over to her quietly and had touched her hot hand. She had opened her eyes and smiled and then she had sat up. Jesus had taken her by the hand and had helped her to rise from the bed. She had been speechless for a moment — hardly daring to believe that she was really well. Then her wonder and gratitude rushed out into words. The Master must sit down and eat with them! He must pass the day with them! In a moment she would have something ready — some fish, cheese, figs, a loaf of bread. "See, I am quite well," she kept exclaiming as she rushed about. "See, the Master healed me!"

The neighbors had hurried home in excitement to report what had happened and soon the news was all over Capharnaum: "Jesus has healed the mother of Simon's wife. She was very sick of a fever!" Word had spread, too, of a cure Jesus had performed that morning in the synagogue; he had cast out an evil spirit from a demented boy.

"You say the boy had an unclean spirit?"

"Yes."

"And was Simon's wife's mother very sick?"

"Yes, she had the look of death."

"Do you think he will cure my son? He was born lame. Where is the Master now?"

"In Simon Peter's house . . . "

And so, soon after sundown, they had started coming, all the lame and blind and sick of Capharnaum — as soon as the Sabbath rest was over. It was a constant procession. Peter did not know there were so many sick in all Galilee. And to think that it had all started with his wife's mother! Peter could hear her now as she moved about among the sick with water for their thirst.

"There, there, my dear. Hush. The Master will heal you soon. See, he will heal you as he healed me. Here, child, take a little water. . . ."

"Just a moment, boy. Jesus is coming your way. Just a moment and he will help you. Have a drink of water, son. . . ."

"She's different," thought Peter. "She was always a good woman, but she is different since Jesus healed her. She's more gentle." When Jesus healed the sick, he healed souls as well as bodies.

Peter's wife was at the door. "Yes, the Master is still here. In just a moment there will be room inside." Peter and Andrew had been helping to carry in the sick and had been occupied with the harder task of clearing people out of the house after they were healed.

"Could you go outside, please, now? Others are waiting. . . ." They all wanted to stay and watch. All night they had done these things and they were tired. Jesus must be tired too, thought Peter, but the Master showed no signs of stopping. He was still alert, still full of sympathy, moving from person to person. Not till the stars had paled and the first faint streaks of dawn were showing in the sky did the last visitors leave.

"Master, you must rest," Peter urged when they were at last alone, but Jesus shook his head. He stood in the doorway, looking from one to another, letting his glance rest lovingly on each one — on Peter first, then on Andrew, on Peter's wife, on her mother, whom he had healed. Then quickly he turned from them and slipped out into the street. Jesus had his own way of resting — alone with his heavenly Father.

Peter stood a moment in the open doorway, looking after Jesus. He was thinking of a passage from the Prophet Isaias which was read sometimes in the Synagogue:

> He himself took up our infirmities,
> and bore the burden of our ills.

Peter slipped out of the house and started down toward the wharf, for Jesus had gone in that direction. There was a hidden spot on the shore of the lake where Jesus liked to go to pray. "That's where he has gone," thought Peter. When he reached the wharf, he found a fair-sized crowd gathered, talking excitedly in spite of the early hour. They were pointing to a figure farther down the beach, standing with his back toward them.

"It's the Rabbi who healed all the sick," they were saying. "It's Jesus, the Master." They turned to Peter: "Simon, you are one of his followers. Go and ask him to speak to us."

Peter hesitated. He could see that Jesus was praying, and besides, he had been healing the sick since yesterday's sundown. But the crowd insisted. "Go on, Simon. Go ask the Master to talk to us." And so, he went on ahead with the crowd following after.

When he reached Jesus, he said, "They are all seeking you."

Jesus shook his head. "I must proclaim the Kingdom of God to the other towns."

"He cannot stay," Peter said, returning to the group. "He is going on to the other towns."

They hung back, hoping he would change his mind; then, seeing he was firm, they started back toward the town. All, that is, but Peter, Andrew, James, and John. They stood there, waiting hesitantly.

Jesus came toward them. "Come," he said, "let us go into the neighboring villages and towns so that I may preach there too."

Their hearts gave a sudden little leap. So — he wanted them with him! He had meant what he said, that morning down by the lake. He really did want them to be fishers of men!

Chapter XII

SIMON THE PHARISEE GIVES
A DINNER

IMON the Pharisee stood in the doorway of his house in Naim, looking out into the spring sunshine. He narrowed his eyes a little to protect them from the glare. There was a wonderful view from his house across the plains of Esdraelon to faraway Mount Thabor. The fields were scarlet with lilies, and the steep streets of the town were terraced with flowering trees. It was no wonder that people nicknamed it "The Beautiful." But Simon the Pharisee was not thinking of the landscape, as he stood in the doorway of his house. He was thinking of the Nazarene who had made such a stir in the town by raising the son of the widow from the dead.

"Are you sure?" he had asked his servant, when the latter had come home in a flurry of excitement to tell his master about it. "Are you sure he wasn't only sleeping?"

But the servant was sure — and well he might be. "They were carrying him to his grave, sir." Jesus had passed the funeral procession on his way into town. He had stopped the procession, and leaning over the body of the young man, he had ordered him to rise. The boy had got up, alive and well, to the astonishment

of all the mourners. No, there could be no mistake. The Nazarene
had raised him from the dead.

Simon the Pharisee had sent his servant about his business, but
he had thought to himself, "This is something worth investigating!"
He had been hearing about this Wonder-Worker for some time —
for over a year, in fact. Simon was a cautious man, a timid man,
but a very curious one. It would not do to go out and mingle
with the common crowd to hear the man speak. He would have
the Nazarene at his house. He would give a banquet for him.
Doubtless, the Master would be flattered, for men said he had been
a common carpenter before he had started preaching.

"Make it a simple supper," Simon said to his servant. "Not the
best wine, you understand. And we will omit the washing of his
feet and the anointing with oil. He doubtless would not expect
them."

"Yes, sir."

"But make it a good dinner."

"Yes, sir."

Simon the Pharisee had rubbed his hands, well pleased.

Now, waiting for his guests to arrive, Simon tried to remember
what he had heard about the Master. The widow's son was the
first instance of his raising the dead to life, but there had been
many cures. "On the Sabbath, too," thought Simon the Pharisee.
There was a paralytic whom Jesus had healed at the Pool of
Bethesda in Jerusalem, and when the Pharisees had accused him
of breaking the Sabbath, he had answered that he was the Lord
of the Sabbath. On another Sabbath, he had cured a man with a
withered hand right in front of the synagogue, openly defying the
Pharisees. "I ask you," he had challenged them, "is it allowed on
the Sabbath day to do good or evil, to save or destroy a soul?"
They had not been able to think of an answer, but they hated him
the more, for lessening their authority.

What was more, the Master definitely favored the poor. His
so-called "Apostles," of whom there were now twelve, were mostly
poor fishermen, with two of his own cousins from Nazareth and a

publican called Matthew. Imagine selecting a publican! The only
man among them of any rank was a fellow named Judas, and
Jesus had not named him head, but a big, uneducated fisherman
called Peter.

"I suppose we should invite his companions too," Simon the
Pharisee had said to his servant. But he certainly did not relish
the thought of sitting down to table with fishermen and a publican!
Well, he would endure it somehow, for the man was worth
investigating.

It was almost time now for them to arrive. Simon came in from
the doorway of his house. It would not do to seem too curious.

*   *   *

Jesus climbed the hill slowly to the hill-top mansion of Simon
the Pharisee. He was in no hurry to reach the house, for he knew
that the invitation had not been made in pure friendliness. It was
much pleasanter to stay out in the mild spring sunshine, talking
with the Twelve. More and more they were beginning to understand the nature of his mission. In fact, he had given them the
power to heal the sick in his name, and to preach the good news of
his kingdom. At first they too thought he had come to establish
an earthly kingdom. They too had been looking for riches and
earthly power. But then, one day, shortly after he had called them
to be his companions, he had taken them, and others of his
followers, out onto a grassy hilltop and had talked and talked to
them, trying to make them understand.

As he had stood in front of them on that grassy knoll, looking
into their upturned, expectant faces, he had been sorry for them:
they were going to be disappointed in his message. They were
thinking: "Is he going to make us rich and free?" "Will he show us
how to throw off the Roman yoke?" "Will he put down Herod
and have himself crowned king?"

His message to them had been just the opposite!

> Blessed are the poor in spirit
>   for theirs is the Kingdom of Heaven.
> Blessed are the meek,

for they shall possess the earth.
Blessed are they who mourn,
    for they shall be comforted.
Blessed are they who hunger and thirst after justice,
    for they shall be satisfied.
Blessed are the merciful
    for they shall obtain mercy.
Blessed are the pure of heart
    for they shall see God.
Blessed are the peacemakers,
    for they shall be called the children of God.
Blessed are they who suffer persecution for justice' sake
    for theirs is the Kingdom of Heaven. . . .

Yes, he was sorry for them. He had gone on and on, explaining to them, trying to make them understand.

As he went up through the streets of Naim toward Simon's house, he thought too of the widow of Naim, whose son he had raised from the dead. She had been so grateful that it had brought the tears to his eyes. There was nothing quite so lovely as gratitude. And the young man, who had been somewhat thoughtless before, now was being kind and thoughtful with his mother. "It would be good to see him," thought Jesus. He always liked to see again a soul whom he had helped, to make sure it did not slip back into its old ways.

He thought too of Mary of Magdala, out of whom he had cast seven devils. She had a wonderful soul, but she needed more help. Her nature was strong and passionate. It needed to be softened and sweetened by sorrow. He thought of her today, because he had caught sight of her, as he was coming into town. A look of recognition had crossed her face, but then she had darted into a doorway. "She will come and seek me out," Jesus said, as he climbed the hill to Simon's house. For he could read her thoughts.

When they reached Simon's house, they waited a moment, breathing deeply the sweet spring air. Then Peter stepped up to the door and knocked. In a moment the servant answered it. Simon came forward, smiling, and rubbing his hands together in the way he had.

"Peace be to this house," Jesus said simply. It was his usual greeting.

"May the God of Israel keep you," answered Simon, bowing. "The Master does my poor house honor." But leading his guests to their places at table, he did not motion his servant to wash their feet, or to pour oil upon their heads, as the custom was at rich men's tables. Jesus made no sign of noticing.

"He does not even know the difference," thought Simon the Pharisee to himself. "He is not used to these finer ways."

But he said, pleasantly enough, to his Guest: "Master, we have been hearing about your preaching and the wonders you have performed. You did our town honor to raise the widow's son from the dead. It is fitting that we should pay honor to you in return."

Jesus answered courteously but with reserve. He knew only too well the cunning of the Pharisees. Their jealousy was growing, and all too often they asked questions just for the purpose of catching him in some contradiction. The time was coming soon when he would denounce them openly for their hypocrisy and for the tyrannical religious burdens which they placed upon the people. But tonight, when he was present as a guest, he would prevent an open argument unless his host left him no other course. Besides, there was some good in the man, and he would put up with all sorts of affronts if there was any possibility of helping a soul.

The dinner passed pleasantly enough, and Simon the Pharisee was congratulating himself on its success, when suddenly the door opened. A woman rushed in, richly dressed, carrying a beautiful alabaster jar. She had a strange, dark beauty, but her clothes were in a certain disarray, as though she were not thinking for the moment about her appearance. Her face had a strong, fixed earnestness.

Simon the Pharisee watched her with horror. Was not this Mary of Magdala? There was hardly a town in lower Galilee, or in Judea either, in her old home of Bethany, where she was not all too well known. For the woman was a sinner. "That's the only word for her," thought Simon the Pharisee. "She is a public sinner!"

To think that she should force her way into his house!

Before he could speak, however, she came quickly toward Jesus and threw herself down on the floor at his feet. She burst into sudden weeping, and her tears flowed down on the feet of Jesus — the feet which Simon had not deigned to wash. Seeing that she had wet his feet with her tears, she leaned over and wiped them with her beautiful long hair. Then, resting back on her heels, she broke the alabaster jar and poured out sweet-smelling ointment on them. In a moment the whole room was filled with its fragrance.

Jesus turned and looked into the woman's sad, tear-stained face. He looked down deep into her soul. It was all washed clean with sorrow and gratitude. It had been, it was true, the soul of a great sinner; but now it was the soul of a saint. He was glad, in his heart, as he looked at her.

Simon, drawing back in disdain, said to himself: "This man, if he were a prophet, would surely know what kind of woman this is who is touching him, for she is a sinner."

Jesus turned toward him, sadly, reading his thoughts. He could not let this chance go by of teaching this proud soul the lesson that it needed. He spoke not in anger, but in love.

"Simon," he said quietly. "I have something to say to you."

"Master, speak."

"A certain moneylender had two debtors. The one owed five hundred pieces of silver, the other fifty. As they had no means of paying, he forgave them both. Which of them, therefore, will love him more?"

"He, I suppose," answered Simon, puzzled, "to whom he forgave more."

"You have judged rightly," Jesus answered quietly, looking steadily at him. "Do you see this woman? I came to your house and you gave me no water for my feet, but she has bathed my feet with tears, and has wiped them with her hair. You gave me no kiss, but she, the moment she entered, has not ceased to kiss my feet. You did not anoint my head with oil, but she has anointed my feet with ointment. Therefore, I say, her sins, many as they are, shall be forgiven her, because she has loved much. But he to whom little is forgiven loves little."

It was one of those rebukes which he knew well how to give — sternly yet kindly. Simon flushed and shifted his gaze. There was nothing he could say. All that Jesus had said was true.

But Jesus turned now to the woman. She was beautiful, with a vivid, exciting kind of beauty; but Jesus was looking only at her soul. It was beautiful now too in its penitence.

"Thy sins are forgiven thee," he said very gently. "Thy faith has saved thee. Go in peace."

She knelt for a moment; then she rose slowly to her feet. She went quickly to the door, without ever raising her eyes, and slipped out. She had humbled herself before them all, but it was worth it, to hear those words. "Thy sins are forgiven thee." They were beautiful, frightening words. For only God can forgive sins.

Jesus went away that night with a glad heart. One more soul had been saved. The angels in heaven would rejoice.

Chapter XIII

THE MOTHER OF JESUS HELPS IN A HIDDEN WAY

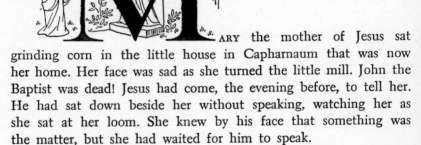 ARY the mother of Jesus sat grinding corn in the little house in Capharnaum that was now her home. Her face was sad as she turned the little mill. John the Baptist was dead! Jesus had come, the evening before, to tell her. He had sat down beside her without speaking, watching her as she sat at her loom. She knew by his face that something was the matter, but she had waited for him to speak.

Presently he had said very quietly: "John the Baptist is dead. Herod had him put to death to please Herodias." Herodias was Herod's brother's wife, whom Herod had taken as his own wife. John had told him it was unlawful, and Herodias had been John's enemy ever since.

Jesus was silent again. His face looked thin and drawn, the way it did when he was greatly troubled. He went out soon afterward into the night, and she knew he had gone somewhere to pray. There was no man he loved so much as John the Baptist. . . .

Jesus did not come to her very often now. She understood. He must be about his Father's business. Those words which he had said as a child of twelve in the Temple were more than ever true. Yet if he was not often with her, she shared that "business" with him. Her part was a hidden one — to stay at home and pray, to do patiently without him, to bear the growing weight of anxiety which she felt for him. She knew that the Pharisees were growing more and more jealous of him, more determined to block his ministry. She knew too that the old prophecies spoke of him as a "Man of Sorrows and acquainted with grief." And of course she would never forget the words of old Simeon in the Temple, thirty-two years before:

> This child is set for the rise and fall of many. . . .
> And thy own soul a sword shall pierce. . . .

But she still had the same answer to God as she had given in Nazareth to the angel:

> Behold the handmaid of the Lord.
> Be it done unto me according to thy word. . . .

She was little more than a child when she first said those words. Now she was no longer young; but her hair was not yet gray, and her body was slender and straight. Those who had not seen her closely sometimes said, "Did you say she is the mother of Jesus? She is very young!"

She shrank from the publicity, but nevertheless she sometimes gathered her cloak around her and went out to hear him preach, when he was speaking in or near Capharnaum. Mary of Cleophas would go with her, and sometimes other relatives. She would stand on the edges of the crowd listening to the precious words which she could understand like no one else:

> Ask, and it shall be given you.
> Seek and you shall find.
> Knock and it shall be opened to you.
> For everyone who asks receives,
>   and he who seeks finds, and to him
>   who knocks it shall be opened.
> For if you, evil as you are, know how
>   to give good gifts to your children,
>   how much more will your Father who is
>   in heaven give good things to those
>   who ask him?

She would watch the puzzled yet eager faces around her. It was strange how hard it was for men to understand that God was good, that he was loving, that he was a Father! Her heart was full of pity as she looked around at those faces.

She tried to lose herself in the crowd as she listened, so that she would not be noticed; but sometimes someone recognized her.

"Isn't this his mother? And those — aren't they his kinsmen?"

Once someone had seen her and had sent a message to Jesus while he was speaking: "Your mother and brethren are standing without, wishing to see you."

He had made of the occasion an opportunity to teach a lesson. He had turned to the crowd and had said:

Who are my mother and my brethren? . . .
Whoever does the will of my Father in heaven,
    he is my brother and my sister and my mother. . . .

Mary had understood. Jesus could not ask anything that she would not understand.

Those whom he helped became her friends too. There was a woman whom he had healed who was pitiful in her gratitude. She had come to Mary to pour out her joy. There was the little daughter of Jairus whom he had raised from the dead. "Look at me! Look — I'm well!" she had cried out excitedly to Mary, as soon as she could run to tell her. "Jesus the Master has cured me!" And she had flung her arms around Mary's neck. "What do you think I can do for him that would please him very much?"

Mary had smiled and had kissed her. "Be a good girl," she had said. "Be a very dear, good girl. That is what will please him most."

The Twelve came to see her sometimes, too — especially Peter and John. They told her what Jesus had been doing.

"Jesus healed a blind man today."

"He raised a widow's son from the dead in Naim."

"He healed the servant of a centurion."

"More and more people are following him. There is even talk of making him king."

Sometimes they came to find where he was. "We haven't seen him since yesterday. Do you know where he is? People are asking for him."

Mary often did not know either, but she could guess. He was still the same Jesus who had spent long nights in prayer on the hilltop above Nazareth.

Mary was thinking of Jesus now as she turned the mill, grinding corn; she was thinking of Jesus and of John the Baptist, who was dead. She was thinking of what the angel had said to Zachary before John was born:

> . . . For he shall be called great before the Lord. . . . And many of the children of Israel he shall bring back to the Lord their God. . . .

It was wonderful what had been happening all over Israel these past two years since John had begun his mission. John had prepared the way, and then Jesus had come. Souls were flocking to him, yet the dividing line was becoming sharper and sharper between those who would and those who would not listen and believe. She was beginning to understand in a new way her own words that she had spoken on the doorstep of Elizabeth's house in Ain-Karim. . . .

> He has put down the mighty from their thrones,
> and has exalted the lowly.
> He has filled the hungry with good things,
> and the rich he has sent away empty. . . .

"But he would not send anyone away empty," thought Mary, leaning over her mill, "except those who refuse to hear." She started to recall again his precious words:

> Ask and you shall receive.
> Seek and you shall find. . . .

Mary stopped her mill a moment and listened. Was that someone knocking at the door? No, there was no sound. She started to turn the mill again. But then once more she stopped. Yes — there was a knock.

She rose to her feet and went to open the door. She stepped back, startled at the beauty of the woman who stood there.

The woman spoke first. "Are you his mother — the mother of the Master from Nazareth? I am Mary — Mary of Magdala. May I come in?"

Mary brought the stranger into the little house. The younger woman looked about her eagerly. So this was the Master's mother! This was her house! It was a poorer house than any Mary of Magdala knew, but it was beautifully cared for. And the woman who was facing her, the woman who was the mother of Jesus, had a wonderful face. She had — how could one put it into words? — a look of very great peace!

Suddenly she found herself down on her knees before the other Mary, pouring out her soul to her. She told of her childhood in Bethany, of her sister Martha and her brother Lazarus. "I was good then," she said, with the tears streaming down her face. "Oh, if I had only stayed good!" She told of her love for the rich young officer of Magdala. And then, in broken phrases, she had told of her descent, step by step, down into a life of sin. . . .

Mary, the mother of Jesus, sat very quietly, listening. She stroked the beautiful hair — the hair that had dried the feet of Jesus.

"Go back home," she said gently, after the pitiful story was finished. "Go back home to Bethany, to the good sister and brother who will help you to be good."

"But the shame! They will not want me!"

"Ah, my child, but now you are different. You are a new Mary. Stay here for a while, if you wish — but then go back. Begin your life again."

The beautiful, dark eyes regarded her thoughtfully.

"You are very much alike, you two," she said softly, more to herself than to Mary. She was silent a moment. Then she spoke again. "Won't Jesus have need of women in carrying on his mission?" She paused, groping for words. "Couldn't a group of women travel to the principal places where he and his disciples are teaching, to care for them?"

Mary smiled, but she did not answer. That was for Jesus to say, not for her. Yet she could see in her mind a little group taking shape — a little group of holy women to help Jesus as only women can. There was Mary of Cleophas, of course. There was Joanna, the wife of Chusa; there was Suzanna; and now there was Mary of Magdala. . . .

The thought was still in her mind, some time later, when she stood in her doorway, saying good-by to Mary Magdalene. "You will come back soon," she said gently. "You will come back and be with me until you are ready to go home to Bethany." But as she watched the slender figure of the younger woman threading her way through the narrow streets, she thought, "She is right. There *is* a work for a group of women to do for Jesus." Standing on the doorstep, looking out over the crooked streets of Capharnaum, she could see, down through the years, a growing company of women who would serve Jesus, and who, in serving him, would become saints.

Chapter XIV

JESUS FEEDS FIVE THOUSAND

AGERLY and noisily the crowd moved along the shore of the lake, northward from Capharnaum. Craftsmen had left their shops, traders their counters, fishermen their boats, housewives their spindles, children their games. A holiday mood had seized them, and they sang and laughed. Every now and then they turned to watch the progress of a boat that was nosing along, ahead of them, with the help of oars. It was trying to pick up a breeze to puff out its sails. It had set out before them, but it was making scant headway.

"It's too heavily loaded," said one of the men, who was a fisherman. But all knew why it was so heavily loaded. It was Simon Peter's boat, and Jesus was in it with the Twelve.

"There's a place up beyond the mouth of the river where he sometimes goes with them," one of the men remarked. That would be a long walk — but they did not mind, not if there was any possibility of overtaking the Master and persuading him to speak to them. They were willing to walk all day if they could hear him tell them more about his kingdom.

Unlike the Scribes and Pharisees and the richer merchants, they found only hope and comfort in his preaching. They were "poor in spirit," these people who hurried along the sandy shore, and poor also in fact. He had promised them that theirs was the kingdom of God. They were meek. He had told them that they would possess the land. Often and often they mourned. He had promised them that they should be comforted. He had told them that those who were least should be greatest in his kingdom, those who were last should be first. To be sure, he had told them to be kind and merciful, to love their enemies, to forgive one another and share what they had. These were harder words; but they were men of good will; they would try. "Be not anxious," he had said, "for your life, what you shall eat, nor for your body, what you shall put on . . . for your heavenly Father knows you have need of these things." They were comforting words.

Sometimes he spoke to them in stories or parables to teach his point. They could not always understand, but they loved to listen. He told of a sower who went out to sow and sowed his seed by the wayside. The birds came along and ate them all. And other seeds fell on rocks and withered away; and some fell among thorns and the thorns choked them. But some fell on good ground and sprang up and yielded a hundredfold. Jesus had smiled at them when he finished that story. "He who has ears to hear," he had said, "let him hear!"

"Explain to us what it means, Master?" his disciples had asked, and he told them that the seed was the word of God. The seeds that fell by the wayside or among thorns represented those who listened but would not believe, or let other matters choke out their good desires. But the good ground stood for those who listened and believed and took to heart the words that Jesus said. They should bear fruit a hundredfold.

"Master, why do you preach that way, in parables?" his disciples asked him sometimes, and he explained it was so that his enemies might not understand, but only his friends. For his enemies might use his words against him.

"To you it is given to know the mystery of the Kingdom of God, but to the rest in parables, that seeing they may not see, and hearing they may not understand." Yet his stories were always of the things they knew — of seeds and bread, of vines and figs, of lamps, of leaven. They could listen to him all day and not grow tired.

And so, they were content, this day, to trudge along the dusty road in the hope of hearing him. Even the old went, and the little children; but the strong aided the weak.

"Granny, do your feet hurt? Here, lean on this staff."

"Thank you, sir. Thank you kindly. The blessing of God be on you."

"Are you tired, little girl? Do you want me to carry you a while?"

"What's that, little boy? You say you brought your lunch? That's more than the rest of us did! We came in too much of a hurry. What did you bring, little boy? Five loaves and two small fishes! Don't tell the bigger boys about it, little lad. The first thing you know, they'll eat your fine lunch!"

"Look, the boat is moving faster. The sails have picked up a breeze. We'll have to hurry if we want to reach the river mouth first!"

People were beginning to drag their feet, and whenever they came to a well, they paused to drink. The sun was higher now, and the day was growing hot.

"There, Granny. You sit down a moment to rest. I'll wait with you!" It was a hard morning's walk. . . .

*   *   *

Peter and the rest of the Twelve had looked forward that day to having Jesus just to themselves. "Come away with me and rest a while," Jesus had said to them that morning in Capharnaum, and he had led them down to Peter's boat. They had a great deal to tell him, for they were back from their first mission. He had sent them off two by two to preach and to heal the sick. It was wonderful what they had been able to do in his name! They had preached; they had healed the lame and the blind; they had even cast out devils. They were eager to tell him all about it.

They had climbed aboard the boat and had rowed it out from shore. But when they put up the sails there was no wind, and they could see the crowd gathering on the shore and starting to follow them. It was always so! In the end, their boat reached the mouth of the river ahead of the foot travelers, but Jesus would not disappoint the crowd. The Twelve, if they were to be like him, must be ready to forget their own desires at the call of souls. "No disciple," he said to them, "is above his Master." They, like him, must learn self-sacrifice.

And so, he gathered the crowd on a grassy hill and talked to them, with the lake shining blue below them and the mountains circling the horizon. Hour after hour he spoke to them, and they scarcely stirred. After a time, he stopped to heal their sick, and then, at their request, he spoke to them again. The shadows lengthened and the sun grew low.

"Why doesn't the Master send them home?" the Twelve said to one another anxiously. "We are far from town and there is nothing for the people to eat." At last they came to Jesus and attracted his attention.

"This is a desert place," they said, "and the hour is already late. Send these people away so that they may go to the farms and villages round about and buy themselves food to eat."

"You yourselves give them some food," Jesus answered, and went on with his preaching.

Give them food? Whatever was the Master saying? There was no food here to give them, and it would take two hundred pieces of silver to buy them all bread! There were five thousand people on that hillside!

Presently, Jesus stopped his preaching, and turning to one of the disciples, he asked, "Is there someone here with anything to eat?"

Andrew gave a dry little laugh. "There is a young boy here with five barley loaves and two fishes. But what are these among so many?"

"Bring them here," Jesus said. "Tell the people to sit down in groups of fifty." The Twelve did as he said, but they were mystified. What was the Master going to do?

"Here, lad," one of the disciples said, going up to the boy.

"The Master would like to have your loaves and fishes."

"Yes, sir." The boy came forward. "Here they are, sir." He looked proud, but just a little wistful — he was very hungry.

Jesus took the loaves and blessed them, looking up to heaven. Then he started to break them. But the more he broke them, the more there was. He motioned to the Twelve to start passing the pieces of bread, and still he went on breaking them. The Twelve passed out the bread, going back and forth among the different groups.

"Look — look at what is happening," people cried out. "Look at the little boy's bread! There is no end to it! There is enough to feed us all!"

Jesus did the same with the fishes. He broke them and passed them too — and they too were enough to feed the whole crowd. In fact, when everyone had finished, there were twelve basketfuls of food left over. Excitement ran high on that grassy hillside. "He has fed us all," the people cried. "He has fed five thousand people with five barley loaves and two fishes! It is the most wonderful miracle of all!" As for the little boy, he was shaking with excitement. "Look at my loaves and fishes," he cried out. "Look at what has happened to them!" He could not believe his eyes.

"This is indeed a prophet," the older people said to one another. "This is the one we have always looked for." Suddenly, someone started shouting: "We want Jesus for our king! Give us Jesus of Nazareth for our king." Others took up the cry. "Give us Jesus for our king!"

Hearing their cry, Jesus turned quickly to the Twelve. "I must go," he said, and almost before they knew what had happened, he had slipped off into the shadows. They knew he would spend the night in the mountains, praying.

At first the people did not notice he was gone. "We want Jesus of Nazareth for our king!" they went on shouting. But when they saw that Jesus was no longer there, they stopped their shouting and started down noisily toward the shore. The Twelve had gone ahead of them and were already climbing into their boat.

"Come, Granny, let me help you down this slope."

"Look out, little girl. This path is steep."

"Here comes the little boy who had the loaves and fishes! Won't your mother be proud!"

So they started back over the way they had come. They straggled along, weary now, and came into town in different groups. Each had his own story to tell — but one thing was certain: Jesus the Master had fed five thousand people with five loaves and two small fishes. There was no one who could deny that it was true!

*   *   *

Darkness came suddenly, that evening, on Lake Genesareth, more suddenly than usual, for a storm was brewing. Peter's boat, with its twelve passengers, rode low in the water. Sharp little waves kept slapping its sides and spilling up over the deck. There was plenty of wind now — too much for safety. It tore the sails and swung the boom around from side to side as it shifted its direction.

Peter and Andrew knew the lake as a scholar knows his book. They knew every cove and beach, every current and shelving ledge of rock. They were not frightened at first. The men sat huddled together near the mast, talking of the day's events. But suddenly a fresh gust of wind pulled at the sail with such force that the boat almost turned over, and water ran over the deck where they were seated.

"Take in the sail," Peter shouted. "Careful, there, careful. Hold — now pull." The wind whipped their clothes about them as they worked. The sail, when they finally pulled it down, was torn.

"Andrew, you and John take to the oars, while I steer." It was heavy going for the rowers. One — two — three — one — two — three — The muscles stood out on their arms and the sweat poured down their shoulders. But the wind was blowing fiercely, and the waves ran high. The boat hardly made any progress at all, for they were pulling against the wind.

There was lightning now, great sheets of it, that lit the dark lake with an eerie glare. Water came into the boat with every wave, and it was riding lower and lower. It was now in real danger of capsizing. If only Jesus were there! They would somehow not be so afraid if he were among them.

One — two — three — The boat was making no headway at all.

Suddenly, as the lightning flashed more brightly than ever, they all stared one way in wonder and fear. A few yards away they saw — No, it could not be true, but it was true! They saw Jesus, close by the boat, walking upon the water! He was walking on those angry, white-tongued waves. All of the Twelve — even Peter — began to shake.

Over the sound of the wind and waves, they heard him say, quietly and firmly: "Take courage. It is I. Do not be afraid."

Seeing that it was, indeed, Jesus, and not some spirit sent to deceive them, Peter, overjoyed, stood up in the boat. He called across the water to Jesus: "Lord, if it is you, bid me come to you over the water."

"Come," Jesus called back, over the sound of the wind.

The others held their breath while Peter climbed over the side of the boat and started walking over the water toward Jesus. Foolish, impulsive, loving Peter! At first he thought only of Jesus. Then, looking down at the angry waves that were licking his legs, he became suddenly afraid. He took one more step. Then he began to sink. He reached out to take hold of the boat, but he had gone too far.

"Lord, save me," he cried out, struggling in the water. But Jesus was close beside him now. He reached out his hand and took hold of Peter.

"Oh, you of little faith, why did you doubt?" He drew Peter toward the boat, and together they climbed into it. Then a strange thing happened. The minute Jesus stepped onto the boat, the wind stopped blowing, the water grew calm, the stars came out in the sky. The storm was over.

The Twelve fell down on their knees before Jesus on the slippery deck of the boat. Truly, this was the Son of God!

The next morning, all at once, their boat appeared at Capharnaum.

The crowd, who were sure they had seen it leave the night before without Jesus, were astonished to see him on board. "Rabbi, how did you come here?" they asked, but Jesus did not answer them.

"I say to you," he said instead, "you seek me, not because you have seen signs, but because you have eaten the loaves and have been filled. Do not labor for the food that perishes, but for that which endures until the life everlasting."

They answered, "Lord, give us always this bread."

But Jesus said to them, "I am the Bread of Life. . . . For I have come down from heaven, not to do my own will, but the will of him who sent me. . . ."

Those who listened murmured among themselves, saying, "Is not this Jesus, the son of Joseph, whose father and mother we know? How does he say, 'I have come down from heaven'?"

But Jesus repeated: "I am the Bread of Life. I am the living bread that has come down from heaven. . . . If anyone eat of this bread, he shall live forever; and the bread I will give is my flesh, for the life of the world."

They were now still more puzzled. "How can this man give us his flesh to eat?"

Jesus did not explain, but he repeated: "Unless you eat the flesh of the Son of Man and drink his blood, you shall not have life in you. He who eats my flesh and drinks my blood has life everlasting. . . ."

"This is a hard saying," people said, one to another. Jesus could see that there were many who did not believe. Indeed, many, from that day, ceased to be his disciples.

Afterward Jesus turned and spoke gently to the Twelve. "Does this scandalize you? Do you also wish to go away?"

In a flash, Peter stepped forward. "Lord, to whom shall we go? You have the words of eternal life."

A look of joy came into the face of Jesus, but then, suddenly, the joy changed to sorrow. "Have I not chosen you, the Twelve," he said, slowly, "and one of you is a devil?"

He turned from them quickly and walked away.

Chapter XV

PETER IS GIVEN THE KEYS
TO HEAVEN

ETER paused a moment for breath
and looked about him. They were traveling through a rough, rocky
country, Jesus and the Twelve. They had left Galilee for a time
and had pushed up north into the region around Caesarea Philippi,
near the headwaters of the Jordan. Jesus did not tell them why
he had come there, but they could guess. His enemies were growing in Galilee. Too many people were saying, "We want Jesus
for our king." Those who were in power did not like it. They
were jealous and afraid.

The Master was not saying much today, and so his companions
were silent too, but they had much to think about. They had been
with Jesus now for more than two years, and the old life seemed
very far away — the life of fishing, of talking outside their houses
in the evening with the neighbors, of living within four walls.
For more than two years they had been moving about with Jesus
from place to place, sometimes in the midst of the crowds that came
to hear him, sometimes off in some mountain canyon where he
had gone to pray.

They had seen him do wonderful things, and had heard him
say words they would never forget. But each year the line was
growing sharper between the people who believed in him and

those who did not. The Pharisees were almost solidly against him
now, except for a very few. Jesus had told strong truths about
them. "You hypocrites," he said to them to their faces; and to
his disciples he said: "Beware the leaven of the Pharisees, which
is hypocrisy." By the leaven he meant their false teachings.

But in the country around Caesarea Philippi, hardly anyone yet
knew Jesus. Only faint rumors had reached them about a Galilean
who healed the sick. For the most part, Jesus was able to travel
around unnoticed. He had spent much time praying, and teaching
the Twelve. Little by little, they were learning about his kingdom.
They were learning that it was not an earthly Kingdom, but a
heavenly one. The great ones in his Kingdom were the ones who
knew how to be humble. He was fond of telling them that they
must become like little children. It was a hard lesson for proud,
grown men to learn.

They were walking now along the edge of a ravine. The water
rushed and gurgled down below, and the trees clung to the rocks
with gnarled roots. It was not like the fertile plains of Galilee.
The Master had been walking along in silence for some time, a
few paces ahead. Peter was next, then James and John. They often
walked in that order. After them came the rest of the Twelve.

Suddenly, as the path broadened out, Jesus turned around and
waited for the others to come up to him. Then he surprised them
by asking: "Who do men say that I am?" He was thinking of the
men round about, who had seen him but little. He had preached
in some of their villages, but not in Caesarea itself, nor in the
wild mountain districts where they now were.

"Some say you are John the Baptist," they answered. "Some
say you are the Prophet Elias, and some the Prophet Jeremias."

Jesus smiled at the rumors. All three of these were dead — two
of them long since; but there was a saying that Elias had not
really died and would return some day to save his people.

Then suddenly, Jesus turned on them and said, "Who do you
say I am?"

They were silent a moment. Then Peter answered slowly, as

though the thought were shaping itself in his mind: "You are the Christ, the Son of the Living God." He had never gone so far as that before.

Jesus stood silent for a moment, gazing far out over the rough, wild landscape. They could see by his face that he was very much pleased. Then he turned to Peter, and said:

Blessed are you, Simon Bar-Jona, for flesh and blood has not revealed this to you, but my Father in heaven.

He paused a moment, as though to emphasize what he was going to say.

And I say to you, you are Peter, and upon this rock I will build my Church, and the gates of hell shall not prevail against it, And whatever you shall bind on earth shall be bound in heaven, and whatever you shall loose on earth shall be loosed in heaven.

Jesus was silent for a moment. They stood looking out over the ravine, Jesus and the Twelve, but their minds were fixed on Jesus' words.

It was Jesus who broke the silence. "Do not say to anyone that I am the Christ." He started again along the rocky road. Presently, he stopped once more and gathered them about him.

"The Son of Man must suffer many things," he said slowly. He often called himself the Son of Man. "He must be rejected by the elders and the chief priests and scribes and be put to death, and on the third day rise again."

He paused and looked from one to another. In each face he could see bewilderment and fear.

What was the Master saying? They had placed all their hope in him. Perhaps they did not expect him to become an earthly king, as some of the Galileans did. But they expected his power to grow and grow. To be sure, he had many enemies, but God was mighty and would put them down in his own good time. That was what they thought — and here was Jesus saying: "He must be rejected . . . and put to death." As for his words about rising on the third day, the disciples were much too bewildered to understand what they might mean.

When they had sufficiently recovered to speak, Peter motioned Jesus to step aside. "Oh, Lord," he said, "this will never happen to you."

Jesus turned to him sternly. "Get behind me, Satan. You are a scandal to me; for you do not mind the things of God, but the things of men." They were hard words; and he had just given Peter charge over his Church. Peter must learn once for all that suffering was a part of God's plan.

But it would take time. He would have to teach them very gradually. He did not say anything more to them about it that day, but a few days later, when there was a larger group of disciples about him, he spoke of it again. This time he hinted at what kind of death he would die. If they wanted to be his followers, they must share it.

If anyone wishes to come after me, let him deny himself, and take up his cross, and follow me. . . .

They looked at one another, bewildered. Was he speaking to them, as he sometimes did, in riddles? They shook their heads; they did not know. There was not one of them who had not seen outside the walls of Jerusalem a row of crosses outlined against the sky. They had seen the bodies of criminals stretched on them to die, and sometimes they had seen some poor fellow being hurried along by a group of Roman soldiers to the place of execution, carrying his cross. The sight was one to strike terror in any man. And here was the Master saying, "Deny yourself, take up your cross, and follow me." They listened, not daring to ask him what he meant.

He watched them struggling to accept this saying. They were not ready yet, he knew; they needed more faith. And so, a few days later, he took aside Peter and James and John, the three who were closest to him. "Come with me," he said, pointing to a mountain that loomed above them. They were not surprised. When he wanted to go apart from the crowds, he often climbed the rocky trail up some mountainside, sometimes alone, other times with some of the Twelve.

They were glad of the prospect of being alone with Jesus. They had been sad lately. The Master had been saying hard, frightening things. Perhaps today he would talk to them more in the old way. And so they followed him expectantly, a few paces behind, as he made his way along the rough path. But today he was silent most of the time, busy, apparently, with his thoughts. "Or perhaps he is praying," thought Peter to himself.

They made good time at first, as they mounted the lower slopes of the mountain. But then the trail grew steep and they went more slowly. John kept close behind Jesus. He was young and nimble. But Peter and James found it harder and kept lagging behind. Jesus turned and waited. It was beautiful to look down over the plain, dotted with villages and farms. To the north lay Lake Genesareth, blue and shining. To the south lay the River Jordan, glittering in its narrow gorge. It was good to stop and look at them.

The trees were growing scrubby now along the trail, and it mounted steeply. Their breath came in quick gasps when they finally reached the top, and they threw themselves gratefully on the ground — all except Jesus. He stood for a time looking out over the valley. Then he shut his eyes as he did when he prayed.

The eyes of his three companions closed too, but not with prayer. The steep climb, the warm air, had made them drowsy. Soon all three of them were sound asleep. They slept for some time; then suddenly they were wakened by a bright light shining in their eyes. That was strange! The sun was far down near the horizon, for the day was drawing to its close. What was this light that was making their eyes blink? Struggling to their feet, they looked about them. They trembled at what they saw.

Jesus was standing where they had left him, but now he was surrounded by light. His face was shining like the sun, so that it hurt their eyes to look, and his garments were whiter than snow. On either side of him was the figure of a man, each one also shining with light. One was Moses, the giver of the Law, and the other was Elias, the greatest of the prophets. The three disciples trembled at the sight.

As the disciples stood gazing, the Master turned toward them a moment. "Lord," exclaimed Peter, stepping excitedly toward him, "it is good for us to be here. Let us set up three tabernacles here, one for thee, and one for Moses, and one for Elias." But while he was still speaking, a bright cloud hovered over them and out of the cloud there came a Voice:

This is my beloved Son in whom I am well pleased. Hear him.

The disciples fell down on their faces, overcome with fear. They had heard such a voice three years before, on the banks of the Jordan, the day Jesus was baptized. But this was more wonderful, more terrifying. The Scriptures had been right in saying, "No man can see God and live."

They lay on the ground for some time, trembling. Then one by one they felt a light touch. They heard the Master's voice, saying: "Arise and do not be afraid." They raised themselves to their knees and opened their eyes. The brightness was gone and they saw no one but Jesus. He was his own kind, gentle self. Their knees were still shaky when they started down the mountain again a short time later. They went in silence, not daring yet to speak. After they had gone some distance, Jesus turned and said, "Tell the vision to no one till the Son of Man be risen from the dead." It was a very great secret to keep from the rest of the Twelve.

They slept that night near the foot of the mountain, wrapped in their cloaks under the glittering stars. The next morning they started early. The rest of the Twelve would be waiting for them; they would be overjoyed to see the Master. "Tell us where you went," they would ask Peter or James or John. "Tell us what Jesus said." Their own hearts would beat faster at the memory, but they would be able to answer only: "We went to the top of the mountain and Jesus prayed."

*　　*　　*

The crowd moved slowly along the road. "He'll come this way," one of the Twelve was saying. "He took the upper trail. We watched him go. Peter and James and John were with him."

"Does the Master often stay on the mountain all night?"

"Yes, often. He goes there to pray."

"Hush, boy, hush!" A man was trying to keep a boy quiet, a great, overgrown fellow who was obviously out of his mind. He kept shouting and twitching and rolling his eyes.

"What's the matter with that boy?" a child asked, holding on tight to his mother.

"Poor boy! He's possessed by a devil."

"Why does he shout like that?"

"Hush, he can't help it. Jesus will cure him."

"Why couldn't those other men cure him?"

"What other men? The disciples of Jesus?"

"Yes, they cured the man with the sore eyes."

"I don't know, dear. Hush, they might hear you. Look, there's Jesus now! There's the Master just coming round the bend with three of his followers."

"May I run to him, mother? See, the other children are running to him. Do you think he'll bless us? He did the children in the other towns."

"Hush, the man wants to go to him — the man with the possessed boy."

The crowd pressed too close for the man to be able to go forward. The poor, tormented lunatic boy shouted and twisted and pulled back.

"Here, let this man through. Let him through with his boy."

It was Andrew who spoke. He piloted the man through the crowd toward Jesus, who had almost reached them and was already surrounded by children. Jesus looked at him kindly.

"Master," the man cried out, with his son pulling at his arm and foaming at the mouth, "I pray you, look at my son, for he is my only child, and a spirit seizes him and he cries out and it throws him down. I prayed your disciples to cast it out but they could not."

Jesus lifted his eyes from the anxious, unhappy face of the father to the crowd which pressed curiously about them. "O unbelieving generation," he said sadly, "how long shall I be with you? How long shall I put up with you?" Then he turned to the man again. "Bring him to me."

The man led him forward, but the boy fell to the ground, twisting and writhing.

"How long is it since this came upon him?"

"From his infancy. Oftentimes it has thrown him into the fire or into the water to destroy him. If you can do anything, have compassion upon us and help us."

The boy rolled and twisted on the ground. The crowd stood very still, waiting. The children stepped back, afraid.

"If you can believe," Jesus said. "All things are possible to him who believes."

"I do believe," the poor man cried. The tears poured down his face. "Help my unbelief."

Then Jesus said very sternly to the spirit that was tormenting the boy, "Thou deaf and dumb spirit, I command thee, go out of him and enter him no more."

The spirit cried out violently and went out of him. The boy lay very still on the ground.

"He is dead," men said to one another. But Jesus took him by the hand and raised him. The boy stood up, pale but well.

For a moment the crowd was silent, awed by what they had seen. Then they broke out into a tumult of excitement. "Look!" they shouted. "See what Jesus has done!"

"Mother, look — the boy is well!"

"Yes, dear. Jesus cured him."

"Mother, may I go to Jesus now?"

"Yes, dear. You may go to him."

It was not till they had reached the town and the crowd had at last dispersed that the disciples of Jesus had him to themselves. When they were alone with him they asked, "Why could we not cast it out?"

He looked at them kindly but sadly. "Because of your little faith. This kind can only be cast out by prayer and fasting."

Chapter XVI

JESUS PREACHES IN THE TEMPLE

 HERE was a great bustle and stir in the little city of Capharnaum, one mellow autumn morning. This was the day that the pilgrims set out for the Feast of Tabernacles. Everyone who could possibly travel went up to Jerusalem for that Feast. Indeed, it was commonly spoken of as the Great Feast.

Since daybreak, people had been assembling, and there was great shouting and moving about in the market place. Hucksters were crying their wares, taking advantage of the gathering crowds to press their sales.

"Figs for the journey, lady."

"Try our dried fish."

Children darted about under the feet of donkeys.

"Watch out, little boys. You are going to get hurt if you don't watch out. You have to watch where you are going."

"It's time to be leaving. The sun is getting high. Is everybody here who is going with the Capharnaum caravan?"

The men looked about them, counting off the people they knew who usually went with the caravan: Jairus, Levi, Jonas, Jesus . . . Where was Jesus? Why wasn't he there with the Twelve? Surely, they would be going to the Feast of Tabernacles!

A man came forward hastily. "No, Jesus isn't coming — not with us." The man's face looked cross and angry.

"Aren't you a relative of his? Can't you persuade him to come with us? We want Jesus."

"I tell you, he isn't coming." The man was plainly annoyed. Indeed, the subject was a sore one with him. He had just been trying to persuade Jesus to come. It would be a wonderful chance for Jesus to come to Jerusalem at just this time with all the Galilean pilgrims to push his cause. Who knows! Perhaps they really could make him king, as they had been suggesting for more than a year — especially if he worked a few miracles in northern Judea on the way down. Whatever possessed him not to come? But when Jesus made up his mind there was no arguing with him. He would answer you quietly, but there was no changing his mind. He had said this time, quietly but firmly, "My time is not yet come."

Now he was keeping carefully out of sight till the caravan had left. It was the only way to avoid notice. The time of his Galilean ministry was drawing to its close. Up and down, up and down, he had gone through the towns and villages of Galilee, and more than ever, Galilee was divided into the two groups of those who did and did not believe. They had had their last chance, these men of Galilee. There would be the Feast of Tabernacles, then the Feast of the Dedication, then the Feast of the Passover. With the Feast of the Passover, his work would be over. He had six months left out of his three years. The leaders in Jerusalem were already plotting his death. He would go up to the Feast of Tabernacles, but he would go in secret, and then, in the time left to him, he would preach in the towns of Judea and across the Jordan. They too must hear the Gospel. He had come to save them too. Nevertheless, his heart was heavy as he watched the Capharnaum pilgrims setting out on their journey without him. He was sorry he would not be with them any more. He loved them — even those who did not believe in him. They were his own people.

* * *

When the Capharnaum pilgrims arrived in Jerusalem, they found the city already crowded. At no time in all the year was there so much excitement in Jerusalem as on the eve of the Feast of

Tabernacles. Its ceremonies recalled the time, centuries before, when the Israelites escaped from Egypt, where they had been in bondage. Now, each year, men put up leafy huts made out of green boughs and slept in them seven nights in memory of their life in the wilderness, after their flight from Egypt. There was great activity making the little tents, and it was a proud day when a Jewish boy was old enough to sleep out in one of these huts with the menfolk. One could lie on one's back and look up through cracks in the leafy roof to the sky, and listen to the singing and laughing, all up and down the streets.

Each day for a week there was a procession down through the streets of the city to the Pool of Siloe to recall the time in the desert when there had been no water and Moses had brought forth water from a rock. A priest filled a golden bowl with water at the pool and carried it back through the streets, with all the people waving palms and singing:

You shall draw water with gladness from the fountain of salvation.

He carried the water back to the Temple and poured it out in the Holy of Holies in thanksgiving to God. It was a beautiful feast, and people came from as far away as Greece and Rome to celebrate it. One could hear them on the street corners, talking in their strange, foreign tongues.

On the first day of the feast, people looked about and said, "Where is Jesus? Isn't he here?" They hoped to see some of his miracles. They looked for him on the second day, on the third day, and still he was not there. Finally on the fourth day they found him. He was standing quietly in the Porch of the Temple, just as though no one had been looking for him.

"Speak to us, Master," they said. "Tell us about the Kingdom of Heaven." And so he spoke to them; but all the time he spoke, there were people in the crowd who kept whispering: "How does this man come by so much learning if he has not studied?"

Jesus turned suddenly toward them. "My teaching is not my own but his who sent me." Then, looking toward some Pharisees who were murmuring against him, he asked, "Why do you seek to put me to death?"

The Pharisees looked embarrassed, but people who knew nothing of the plots against him exclaimed, "Who seeks to put you to death?"

Jesus stood regarding them sadly. There was so little he could say to them, in the midst of all that murmuring! "A little while I am with you," he said to them, puzzling them still further, "and then I go to him who sent me, and where I go you cannot come."

The people said among themselves, "Where is he going that we cannot find him?" In the midst of their clamor, Jesus slipped quietly away and went out of the crowd. There was so much he wanted to tell them while he still could! In a little while it would be too late. Moses had given his people water in the desert; Jesus would give them living water — the water of grace. If they would only listen! His heart was heavy with longing.

On the last day of the feast he stood among them in the great, crowded portico of the Temple. For seven days the procession had gone down through the streets of the city to the Pool of Siloe. This was the eighth day and there would be no procession. Standing before the crowd, close to the place where the priest had passed with his golden bowl of water, Jesus cried out in a loud voice:

If anyone thirsts, let him come to me and drink.
He who believes in me, as the Scripture says,
    from within him there shall flow rivers of living water.

The crowd, overcome with surprise, stood very still. Then someone cried out, "This is truly a prophet! This is the Christ!" Others took up the cry: "This is the Christ!" But then people started murmuring again. "Can the Christ come from Galilee? Does not the Scripture say that it is from Bethlehem, David's city, that the Christ is to come?"

Such great division broke out that the chief priests and Pharisees thought the time had come to seize him. They sent the Temple attendants out to lay hold of him, but they came back empty-handed.

"Where is the Galilean?" the Pharisees demanded angrily.

The attendants were full of wonder. "Never has any man spoken as this man," they said.

The Pharisees scoffed. "Have you also been led astray? Have any of the rulers believed in him, or any of the Pharisees, but only the common crowd, who do not know the Law?"

Suddenly one of the Pharisees came forward, and stood facing them. It was Nicodemus, pale but determined, who had visited Jesus by night nearly three years before. He had been afraid then to be seen with Jesus. Now he was ready at last to defend him. He said quietly, "Does our Law judge a man unless it first gives him a hearing and knows what he does?"

They only jeered at him. "Are you also a Galilean?" they asked scornfully. "Search the Scriptures and see that out of Galilee arises no prophet." Nicodemus was silenced for the moment; but his mind was made up. He would help Jesus, whatever it might cost. He had at last been "born again."

The Pharisees gave up the chase for the time being. There were still too many who supported him. They would have to find some way of tricking Jesus so that he would lose favor with the crowd.

Jesus slipped off to the Mount of Olives to pray. Sometimes he prayed in the Garden of Gethsemani, sometimes farther up the hill, where he could look out over the city that he loved. He prayed all night, and at daybreak he came again into the Temple. He was standing in the portico, looking out over the city, when the first visitors found him and clamored for him to speak. In a moment a crowd formed and he sat on one of the great stone benches and taught them.

Suddenly they were disturbed by angry voices. The crowd turned round to see Temple attendants dragging a woman toward Jesus, surrounded by Scribes and Pharisees.

"Master," one of the Pharisees said, "this woman has just now been caught committing sin. In the Law Moses commanded us to stone such persons. What do you say?" It was a trick to catch him. The law had not been enforced for generations, but if he suggested setting it aside, they would say: "He denies the Law of Moses."

Jesus stooped down and began writing with his finger on the ground. Then he straightened up slowly and looked at them. They watched him closely, like hawks watching their prey.

"Let him who is without sin among you cast the first stone," he said very quietly. Then, leaning over again, he went on writing on the ground. One by one, beginning with the eldest, the Pharisees departed. When they had all gone, Jesus looked up at the woman. She stood before him, trembling.

"Woman," he said very gently, "where are they? Has no one condemned thee?"

"No one, Lord."

"Neither will I condemn thee. Go thy way and sin no more."

A look of bewilderment crossed her face, followed by a look of wonder. Could it be true? Had the Pharisees all gone, and had the Master really forgiven her? Jesus, watching her kindly, knew that he had not only won a victory over the Pharisees. He had done something much greater; he had saved a soul.

Soon the people crowded around him again. "Teach us, Master," they pleaded. He seated himself in the Treasury and they gathered around him. He looked at their eager, upturned faces. There was so much he wanted to say while he was yet with them! He began, knowing that the Pharisees would soon be breaking in upon him once more.

"I am the light of the world," he said. "He who follows me will not walk in darkness but will have the light of life."

There was a shuffling of feet behind him, and the proud voice of a Pharisee broke in: "You bear witness to yourself. Your witness is not true!"

He answered the Pharisee, and then he went on speaking, for the time had not yet come when they could harm him.

If you abide in my word, you shall be my disciples, and you shall know the truth, and the truth shall make you free.

Because I speak the truth, you do not believe me. But which of you can convict me of sin?

If I glorify myself, my glory is nothing. It is my Father who glorifies me, of whom you say that he is your God.

Many listened and were moved, but others picked up stones to cast at him. Jesus slipped away, as they were arguing, and went sadly out of the Temple. He would go back to the country, where people were simple and humble. They, at least, would listen and believe.

Chapter XVII

JESUS RAISES LAZARUS FROM THE DEAD

ANDALED feet moved softly through the house of Lazarus with a kind of hushed excitement. It was very different from the joyous excitement of a few weeks before, when Jesus the Master had been there with the Twelve for the Feast of the Dedication.

If only Jesus were here now, thought Mary, the sister of Lazarus, as she sat beside him, bathing his face with cold water from the well. Jesus would heal him, as he had healed her, as he had healed their neighbor, Simon the Leper. He would say, "Lazarus, arise!" taking him by the hand, and Lazarus would rise, sound and well again, with his fever all gone and the old smile on his face.

But Jesus was not here, and Lazarus was tossing and turning on his bed, and calling for "Water! Water!" He was turning his head away from the food that Martha brought and was growing weaker each day.

"How is the young master today?" the neighbors asked each morning.

"No better, thank you, neighbor. His fever is burning and he won't eat." They were weary of making the same reply.

If only Jesus were here, if only . . . Mary wrung out the linen

117

cloth from the cold water and laid it on her brother's hot head. If only . . .

Then suddenly she sat up very straight and her face brightened.

Perhaps Jesus was not too far away! Perhaps they could send for him, and he would come. Or perhaps, without coming, he would heal Lazarus at a distance, the way he had done with the centurion's servant in Galilee. "Lord, I am not worthy that you should enter under my roof. Say but the word and my servant shall be healed," the centurion had said. Jesus, in Cana, had said the word, and the servant in Capharnaum was well. Perhaps he would do that with Lazarus. . . .

She rose and hurried over to Martha, who was stirring a pot.

"Martha, we could send for Jesus. It isn't too late."

Martha straightened up and regarded her sister. "We don't know where he is."

Mary was not to be put off by difficulties, now that her mind was made up. "He was headed east, men said, toward the Jordan."

It was a rather wild errand to go riding across the land in search of someone whose whereabouts one did not know. But it was worth trying. Anything was worth trying!

Mary called their servant, a dark, silent fellow with honest eyes.

"Do you think you can find Jesus, the Master?"

He blinked a little and swallowed. Then he nodded. "I will try, my lady," he answered, bowing.

"We don't know where he is, but he was headed toward the Jordan."

"Yes, my lady."

"Take your master's donkey, and when you find him, bid him come. No — say to him, 'The one whom you love is sick.' "

"Yes, my lady."

"And ride hard."

"Yes, my lady." His dark eyes glowed. He loved his young master, Lazarus, but even more he loved the Galilean Master. There was no one who ever came to the house who was like him.

*   *   *

Jesus sat waiting in the sharp winter air for his disciples to return. The winds blew across the Jordan valley from the mountains. He drew his cloak about him, smiling to himself.

This was the day when the seventy-two were to return from their first mission. He had chosen them from the people who had followed him so faithfully through Galilee, and he had sent them out like the Twelve, two by two, to preach in his name. Soon he was going to have to leave them — in less than six months. He must let them test themselves while he was still with them. They must feel the power of working in his name. So they had set forth, soberly and a little fearfully, and now they were coming back, two by two as they had gone. Scanning the horizon, he caught sight of them, coming over the rough Judean road, dusty, tired, but eager. Their manner of walking showed they had been successful.

Over the same road he could see another figure, farther off — the figure of a man with a dark face, a rough mantle, and anxious eyes, riding a limping donkey. The sides of the donkey were sore where he had dug in his heels to try to make him go faster. For his errand was one of life and death.

Poor Lazarus who was dying! Poor Mary and Martha, leaning wearily over him, praying for Jesus to come!

Dear Jesus, come quickly. . . .

Or say but the word, that our brother shall be healed. . . .

Jesus could see them, in faraway Bethany, Jesus who was God and man. It was going to be hard to hurt them. They were most loving, most trusting, but they would not understand. Not at first! Afterward they would be glad and thankful at this new proof of the power and goodness of God. . . .

Up the road came the seventy-two, and across the grassy stretch to the knoll where Jesus was sitting. He greeted them and they dropped down at his feet. They could hardly wait to report their adventures to him. They had done wonderful things. They had preached; they had healed the sick; they had even cast out devils.

That seemed to them the most wonderful thing of all. "Lord," they said, "even the devils are subject to us in thy name." They were like children in their eagerness.

Jesus looked out thoughtfully over the countryside. "I was watching Satan fall as lightning from heaven," he said slowly. Then he turned to them and said kindly but sternly: "Behold I give you power over the power of the enemy, and nothing shall hurt you. Yet do not rejoice in this, that the spirits are subject to you, but in this, that your names are written in heaven." Then, raising his eyes, he prayed, aloud so they too could hear:

I praise thee, Father, Lord of heaven and earth that thou didst hide these things from the wise and prudent and didst reveal them to little ones. . . .

When he turned to them again, his face was very gentle. He was thinking of them and of how much they would have to suffer because of him. He was thinking, too, of that hard-pressed man on the donkey, and of two sisters at the bedside of their brother in Bethany. He was thinking of all weary and sorrowing souls, up until the end of time.

"Come to me, all you who labor and are overburdened," he said very gently, "and I will give you rest. Take my yoke upon you and learn of me, for I am meek and humble of heart; and you will find rest in your souls."

Jesus was looking at them, and beyond them, at the man climbing down from a tired donkey and tying it to a tree. Now he was coming forward, stumbling a little for weariness.

It had not been easy for the servant of Lazarus to get on the track of Jesus. Everywhere he asked, "Has Jesus been this way, Jesus the Galilean?"

"Yes, he cured ten lepers," they said to him in one place, but that had been no help, for that was before the Feast of the Dedication, when Jesus had been in Bethany.

"Yes, he told us a story about laborers in a vineyard," they said in another. But that too was some time earlier. At last he came to a place where men said, "Yes, he was here yesterday. He is staying down by the ford of the Jordan." When the servant heard that, he pushed on his donkey harder. He was almost at his journey's end. He would speak to Jesus, and the Master would come with him; or he might only say the word and Lazarus would be healed. That is the more likely, thought the servant, coming toward Jesus, considering how far they were from Bethany.

As the man came forward, Jesus looked at him and smiled. It was almost as though he expected this thing to happen! That is strange, thought the servant. Bowing, he delivered his message, which he had been rehearsing over and over in his mind through all those weary miles. "Master, I have been bidden to say to you, the one whom you love is sick."

Jesus listened kindly, and then he turned to his disciples. "This sickness is not unto death," he said, "but for the glory of God, that through it the Son of God may be glorified."

The anxious face of the servant brightened as he heard those words. His young master was not going to die! Jesus would heal him. Perhaps he had already done so just by his words, as he had healed the centurion's servant. Perhaps Lazarus was already sitting up on his bed and smiling to his sisters. Glory be to God, thought the servant. Glory be to the God of Israel!

He bowed and kissed the robe of Jesus. Then he went back across the dry grass to the place where his donkey was tied. He must hurry home with the good news. He must hurry home to Lazarus and his two sisters. Glory be to God!

When he reached home, Lazarus was dead.

Jesus waited two days by the Jordan, showing no signs of leaving. The disciples were not surprised, since Lazarus was not in any danger. Besides, it was no longer safe for Jesus to be so near to Jerusalem. At the Feast of the Dedication, the Pharisees had tried to stone him, just as they had tried to do at the close of the Feast of Tabernacles. But then suddenly, on the third day after the servant's departure, Jesus said to them, "Come, let us go into Judea."

They were immediately anxious. "Master, when you were there before, the Jews were seeking to stone you. Are you going there again?"

But Jesus insisted, and so they started off.

As he walked along, he seemed to have something on his mind, for he was very silent. After a little distance, he said, "Lazarus, our friend, is sleeping. But I am going to wake him from sleep."

So that was why he was going! He was going to see Lazarus! They tried again to persuade him not to go. "Lord, if he is sleeping, he is safe."

Then Jesus spoke out plainly. "Lazarus is dead." Then he added mysteriously, "I rejoice on your account I was not there, so that you may believe. But let us go to him."

They took the straightest route across Judea, avoiding the larger towns because of the danger. But by the time they reached Bethany, Lazarus had been dead four days. Friends of Martha and Mary, who were on their way to the house to comfort the two sisters, saw Jesus and the Twelve, and they hurried with their news.

"Jesus is here," they said excitedly. "He is just coming into town."

The sisters looked up with hopeful faces. This was the first good news they had had since their brother fell ill. Yet they could not help saying to themselves, even though they loved Jesus very much, "If he had only, only come sooner! Surely, he would have healed Lazarus!" Each day after they had sent their servant to Jesus, they said to each other, "Today, Jesus will come. He will cure Lazarus." But each day Lazarus grew weaker, his fever burned hotter, and Jesus did not come. Finally Lazarus died, and the servant came back with his message from Jesus — the message that was not true, for Lazarus' sickness had been "unto death." Mary and Martha did not know what to think. And now at last Jesus had come — too late.

Martha got up quietly and went out of the house. Looking down the street, she could see the group coming toward her along the dusty road. She did not know which was uppermost in her mind, sorrow or joy, as she hurried along the road to meet them. Then she stood still and waited for Jesus to come.

"Lord," she said to him quietly, when he reached her, "if you had been here, my brother would not have died."

Martha was silent a moment; a thought was dawning in her sad, troubled mind. Then she said slowly, "But even now I know that whatever you shall ask of God, God will give it to you."

Jesus looked at her lovingly. "Your brother shall rise," he said gently.

"I know he will rise at the resurrection — at the last day."

He saw that she did not understand. "I am the resurrection and the life," he said slowly, emphasizing each word. "He who believes in me, even if he dies, shall live, and whoever lives and believes in me shall never die."

He studied her face as he spoke. It did not change from its look of bewildered grief. But he rejoiced at her answer.

"Yes, Lord, I believe you are the Christ, the Son of God, who have come into the world."

It was a tremendous act of faith, but she still did not understand what he was trying to tell her. She would have to wait and see with her own eyes.

She turned from him and went ahead into the house.

"Mary," she said, "the Master is here and is calling for you."

Mary lifted up her tear-stained face questioningly, as though at first she had not heard quite clearly. Then, with an effort, she collected her thoughts. The Master was here — Jesus. She rose quickly and hurried out to meet him. But when she saw him, she fell down at his feet, and she too said, "Master, if you had been here, my brother would not have died."

Her troubled face cut Jesus to the quick. He loved Mary and Martha, and their brother Lazarus. He loved them and he had hurt them — but he had done it for their sake and for the sake of the whole world.

"Where have you laid him?" he asked quietly.

"Lord, come and see." She led him out to the edge of town where the tomb was.

People saw them go and followed after. "The Master is going to the tomb," they said. "He is going there to mourn with Mary and Martha." Others came out of their houses and followed after. "Jesus, the Galilean, is going to the tomb of Lazarus." But a few said, "If he loved Lazarus so much, why didn't he come and heal him?"

They stood in a circle as Jesus stepped toward the tomb. He paused and looked at the sealed door, and then at the weeping sisters. The tears came into his own eyes, and bowing his head, he wept.

"See how he loved him," the people said, one to another; but some few said, "Could not he who opened the eyes of the blind have caused that this man should not die?" Even here, Jesus had his enemies as well as his friends.

Jesus came closer to the tomb. It was carved into the rock and was sealed by a stone.

"Take away the stone," he said.

"He is four days dead," Martha protested.

Jesus said to her gently, "Have I not told you that if you believe you shall behold the glory of God?"

She looked at him, bewildered, but gave the command to roll away the stone. When it had been pushed aside, Jesus lifted up his eyes and prayed. Then he cried out in a loud voice: "Lazarus, come forth."

The crowd stood breathless, waiting. Suddenly Lazarus stirred. People turned pale as they saw. Then he raised himself. Slowly he got up from the place where they had laid him, still bound in his grave clothes.

"Unbind him and let him go," Jesus said.

Trembling, they did so. Lazarus stood before them, blinking a little, as though trying to remember what had happened. The people stood silent a moment, dazed; then they rushed forward shouting. "Lazarus lives!" "The Master has raised Lazarus from the dead!" "Jesus of Nazareth has raised up a man four days in the tomb!" They started back toward the town, shouting and cheering. Soon everyone knew in Bethany, and before night the news had reached Jerusalem. "Jesus, the Galilean, has done the most wonderful thing yet! He has raised to life a man four days dead." If Jesus had hoped to remain in Judea unnoticed, he certainly had not succeeded! But of course, he had known all along that it would be this way.

When Mary and Martha first saw that their brother lived, they were speechless. Then gradually, their fear and wonder turned to joy. He had not failed them, the Master! They had both reproached him, and their Lord had repaid them like this — with never a word of rebuke! Surely, Martha had been right when she said: "You are the Christ, the Son of God."

Chapter XVIII

JESUS MAKES TWO STOPS
IN JERICHO

T WAS spring in Judea, and the roads were full of pilgrims, heading toward Jerusalem for the Feast of the Passover. West from the Jordan they came, south from Galilee, inland from the sea.

Jesus, from his refuge in the quiet hill town of Ephrem on the edge of the desert, had watched winter turn to spring. He had seen the valley grow green, the days lengthen, the old moon wane and the new moon come. It was time to leave Ephrem and move south to Jerusalem. It was time to go there to die.

It was fitting that he should die at the time of the Passover. It too, like the Feast of Tabernacles, recalled the escape of the Jews from Egypt. Before leaving the land of exile, each Jewish family had been warned to slay a lamb and sprinkle its blood on the doorposts of the house. For an angel of God was coming to slay the first-born sons of the Egyptians in punishment for their sins. It would pass over the houses where the blood was sprinkled. Ever since then, in each Jewish household, at the Feast of the Passover, a lamb was slain and eaten with unleavened bread in thanksgiving. But a new lamb was going now to be slain — Jesus whom John the Baptist had called the Lamb of God. "Behold the Lamb of God," he had said of Jesus, "who takes away the sins of the world."

Jesus prayed long one night in the little town of Ephrem, and the next morning he called his disciples together and they started down the rough hill road. He was silent for a while as he walked, looking at the faces around him. There was big, blustering, loving Peter, walking with his head bent forward, in the way he had. There was Peter's brother Andrew, like Peter only quieter. There were the brothers James and John, so warm and ardent that he had called them Sons of Thunder. After them came Nathanael, Thomas, the cautious one, James the Younger and Jude, his cousins, and Matthew, the publican. Last of all came Judas, regarding the ground darkly, as though he had something on his mind. Judas had changed in the last few months. There was something cloudy about his face, a slight shiftiness about his eyes. Jesus sighed as he looked at the face of Judas.

They were all so unsuspecting, the Twelve, as they trudged along the dusty road that mild spring day. Again and again he had tried to warn them. "Behold," he had said, "we are going up to Jerusalem and all things that have been written through the prophets concerning the Son of Man will be accomplished. For he will be delivered to the Gentiles, and will be mocked and scourged and spit upon, and after they have scourged him, they will put him to death; and on the third day he will rise again." He had seen from their faces that they did not understand, and only a little later, they had fallen to arguing as to which should be greatest in his kingdom! But he must be patient with them, very patient. They had hard days ahead.

As they moved along through the towns and villages of Judea, people came to the doors of their houses and called out: "It's Jesus, the Master, the one who raised a man four days dead." "It's Jesus of Nazareth, going to the Feast!" Men rushed back into their houses, grabbed up a few provisions in a basket, and started hurrying after him. "We're going with Jesus," they called out to their neighbors. "He's going to Jerusalem for the Feast!" And so, as

Jesus and his followers moved south toward Jerusalem, the crowd grew hour by hour. Men followed him; women followed him; children with sticky fingers and tousled hair followed him; dogs raced around, barking. He was escorted by a multitude by the time he reached the outskirts of Jericho.

"It's Jesus!" the men of Jericho cried out, seeing the crowd coming. "It's Jesus who raised Lazarus from the dead!" For Jericho was close to Bethany, and they knew Lazarus by name.

Jesus was talking to the crowd as he came into Jericho. People were listening intently, but it was hard to hear over the shuffle of many feet, the barking of dogs, the babbling of babies. "Hush, be quiet! We want to hear!"

Blind Bartimeus sat by the side of the road, holding up his begging bowl. He had sat in that same spot ever since the people of Jericho could remember. It was a good location for begging. People got out their purses to pay their toll at the tollgate, and it was easy to drop a coin into his bowl.

A penny, please, a penny! A penny for a poor blind beggar.
A penny for the love of God!
A penny, please, a penny.

There was a clink in the brass bowl.

"Oh, thank you, sir, thank you. May the God of Israel bless you."

"A penny, please, a penny."

There was good business today, for travel was heavy, and just before the Feast people were generous. But lean times were coming; he must get as much as he could.

"A penny for an old blind beggar."

The warm spring sun felt good on his head, but the wind was sharp. He drew in closer to the wall.

"A penny for the love of God."

He listened to the jingle of camel bells as caravans of merchants came by from the north. They had no time for a poor blind beggar by the road to Jericho. Then he heard the jingle of a horse's trappings. That would be some officer of Caesar. And then he heard — what did he hear? The shuffle of many feet, the sound of many people, and yet over them all there came the sound of one voice, clear and ringing on the sun-warmed air.

"Please, sir, what's happening down the road? Who is that coming toward us?" he asked of someone who was passing him on foot.

"It's Jesus," the man answered, "Jesus, the Galilean! It's the one who raised Lazarus from the dead."

"That was a wonderful thing! What else has he done?"

"Oh, he cured a paralytic, and he healed ten lepers — many, many things! I can't begin to tell you all he's done."

"Did he ever give sight to the blind?"

"Yes, he did that, you may be sure."

Bartimeus sat very still by the gate of Jericho. He forgot to hold out his bowl. Jesus, who had raised the dead, was coming! He could give sight to the blind. A sudden hope stirred within him. What would it be like to see? To see flowers, and ripe fields, and the faces of good men and women? What would it be like to see the stars?

The sounds came closer and closer. The first of the crowd were passing him now, and the clear, kind voice was just above him — the voice of the wonderful Master!

Bartimeus raised himself, the pulses beating wildly in his forehead, in his neck. His hands were cold with excitement.

He cried out with all his force: "Jesus, Son of David, have mercy on me." His voice was drowned in the crowd. He called out still louder, cupping his mouth with his hands. "Jesus, Son of David, have mercy on me."

"Silence, there, fellow, silence," voices called to him. "You are interrupting the Master."

Tears came to the sightless eyes of Bartimeus. He couldn't let this chance pass — he couldn't! It might never come to him again.

"Jesus, Son of David, have mercy on me."

Suddenly, there was silence. The shuffling feet stopped, and the kindest voice he had ever heard said quietly. "Bring him to me."

The men who had shouted at him were all politeness now. "Come, friend," they said, "The Master is calling you."

He pulled himself stiffly to his feet and started groping his way toward the voice. Big hands took hold of him and led him. Then the kind voice spoke again.

"What did you wish that I do for you?"

Suddenly, he began to tremble. "Lord, that I may see!" he cried. There was a terrible, torturing moment when the beating of his heart almost choked him. Then the kind voice said very gently, "Go, your faith has saved you."

Suddenly, the daylight blazed upon him. He opened his eyes and shut them again — it was too bright. Then he opened them again more cautiously. He could see — and he was looking up into the kindest face in all the world. It was even kinder than the voice.

"Glory be to God!" he cried out. "Glory be to the God of Israel." The tears ran down his cheeks. "Glory be to Jesus, Son of David." He hardly knew what he was saying.

He was caught up by the crowd, and they cheered and shouted. "Look at the man that Jesus healed. Look at blind Bartimeus, who can see!" They carried him with them into Jericho.

"Master," he said, when the crowd had quieted down, and he could get close to Jesus, "Master, I will follow you all the days of my life." Jesus looked at him and smiled. It was good to see someone who was grateful for the gifts of God.

*   *   *

The time just before the big feasts was always a busy one for Zacchaeus, the chief publican of Jericho. More taxes were paid and more tolls were taken than at any other time of the year. Zacchaeus was honest and prudent for a publican. Perhaps once in a while he took a little extra, beyond what he should — but after all a man deserved what he could get when he watched his business carefully. So thought Zacchaeus as he hurried through the streets of Jericho, from one agent to another, to see that all were attending to their business. Now if all publicans were as zealous and prudent, thought Zacchaeus, publicans would not have so bad a name! He rubbed his hands together and smiled to himself, and he was very well pleased.

People nodded as he passed. They all knew the little man with the brisk way of walking and the broad smile. He was not quite five feet tall, but he had a good head on his shoulders, that Zacchaeus, the chief publican of Jericho! At least, so people said. He hurried toward the east gate of the city, where he had an agent stationed to catch the traffic from the north and east. The man needed watching; he took more for himself than was decent, even for a publican. For, as the saying goes, there is honor even among thieves.

The travel that day was unusually heavy, even for the Passover season. There seemed to be a lot of foot passengers all traveling together — more than one would expect for a single caravan of pilgrims. They looked to be a rather poor sort of crowd. They wouldn't bring in much business for the publicans! And yet, something about the crowd attracted Zacchaeus, and he turned and stood staring up the road.

"Who are all those people?" he asked a passing merchant.

"What! Don't you know? That's Jesus coming, the Galilean, and those are his followers."

"Jesus, the Galilean? The one who raised Lazarus from the dead?"

"Yes, the same man."

"And didn't I hear he called a publican to be one of his disciples?"

"I dare say you did. They say he eats with publicans and sinners."

There was a little dig in the last remark, but Zacchaeus was growing too excited to notice. He wanted to see this Jesus.

But the people were coming closer and closer, and he was not quite five feet tall. What chance would he have to see Jesus, over all that crowd? What was that they were shouting? "The Master has cured blind Bartimeus! He has given him his sight!"

Now, more than ever, Zacchaeus wanted to see. Even on tiptoe, he could not get even a glimpse of the Master. He looked about for something to stand on — some stone or mound; there was nothing. But along the road there was a row of sycamore trees, with low, inviting branches. He glanced about to see if anyone was looking, and scrambled up into the nearest tree. Then awkwardly, puffing and panting, he turned himself about. It was many a year since the publican Zacchaeus had climbed a tree!

When he had got himself settled, he looked down. He was well above the crowd in his leafy lookout, and he could easily see Jesus coming along. "He looks very kind," Zacchaeus thought, "not the sort to stand on ceremony. Perhaps he really did eat with publicans!"

Suddenly, as Zacchaeus was staring down through the branches, the Master turned and looked square at him. A slow smile crossed the kind face.

"Zacchaeus," he said, "come down quickly, for today I must stay in your house." Zacchaeus nearly fell out of the tree. When he had got over his first surprise, he scrambled down, gave his rumpled clothes a hasty pat, and hurried toward Jesus. This time the crowd opened and let him pass. That is how Zacchaeus, the publican, came to entertain Jesus, the Master, in his house. It was a story he loved to tell ever after.

As Zacchaeus sat with Jesus that day in his comfortable Jericho home, passing the Master the lamb, the cheese, the wine, he had a strange feeling of being in a dream. Was this happening to him, Zacchaeus, the publican? And a queer thing happened as they sat together. The eyes of this man Jesus seemed to look clear through him. They seemed to be searching him to the depths of his soul. And as he felt those eyes upon him, Zacchaeus grew more and more uneasy. Was he sure he had not traded unjustly? Was there any corner of his soul he was ashamed for those eyes to see?

Finally, Zacchaeus could bear that doubt no longer. "Lord," he said, "I am going to give half my goods to the poor, and if I have done any wrong to anyone, I am making fourfold amends."

A look of sudden joy came into the face of Jesus. "Today salvation has come into this house," he said, his face still shining. "The Son of Man has come to seek and to save what was lost."

Chapter XIX

MARY MAGDALEN BREAKS A JAR OF PERFUME

IMON the Leper looked with satisfaction about the room. The supper for Jesus was going nicely. Martha, the sister of Lazarus, was helping to serve, and she always did everything well. Lazarus was there too. People all wanted to see him, now that he had been raised from the dead. Wherever he went, one could hear people saying in low tones: "He looks very natural, doesn't he! But he seems quieter." It was getting to be somewhat of a nuisance in Bethany, this constant procession of people coming to look at Lazarus. Friends came, and even strangers. They hung around outside the house, hoping to see him. "Is this the man who was four days dead?" they would ask. But tonight the guests were all friends of the Master — the Twelve and a few others.

They had come for the Passover, and were staying in Bethany. Simon had been proud to ask them to dine, Simon who was still called "the Leper" although he had been cured. He looked sometimes at his hands in wonder, at the good sound skin where the ugly sores had been. The priests in the Temple had said he would have to go and live outside the town with the other lepers. He still shuddered at the thought. One could see them by the roadside with their poor deformed hands and feet showing beneath their rags. The Lord had been very good to him and he was grateful. His eyes rested lovingly now on Jesus, as he looked about at his guests. Yes, the Lord had been very good.

It was whispered that there were plots against Jesus and that he had taken his life in his hands to come to Jerusalem for the feast. Perhaps that was why he was staying in Bethany instead of in Jerusalem — to throw men off his track. Or perhaps he was just there because he loved Lazarus and Martha and Mary. How could anyone want to do him any harm? Simon looked at Lazarus, sitting at his left, so well and radiant. There were hundreds, all over Palestine, who had been made whole and new again by Jesus. And then he looked at Mary, out of whom Jesus had cast seven devils. That was a still more wonderful thing! She was sitting beside the door, her eyes fixed on the Master's face, drinking in his words. She understands him better than anyone, thought Simon, and look what she was before! It was an even greater thing to heal men's souls than to cure their bodies! How could anyone not believe he was the Christ?

*   *   *

Mary Magdalen, sitting beside the door in the house of Simon the Leper, was strangely stirred. It was the first time she had been with Jesus since he had raised Lazarus from the dead. She had been so silent that day — she was too stunned to speak. And to think how close she had come to doubting him! She could not get those words of hers out of her mind: "Master, if you had been here, my brother would not have died." They were almost a rebuke, and she had said them to Jesus! She had said them to her Lord and Master, the Son of the Living God! And he had been so forgiving, so understanding! Never a rebuke for her lack of faith, only compassion for her sorrow. How could she ever make amends?

Her mind went back over the time she had known him. She thought of that first day when the touch of his hand sent the devils out of her tormented body and left her in peace. She thought of the time in the house of Simon the Pharisee when she anointed his feet with perfume and he lifted from her the burden of her sins. It was strange that she had done that in a house of a man named Simon — and here again she was in a Simon's house. But such a different Simon! She thought too of those days in Galilee when she and the other women followed Jesus, ministering to him and to the Twelve. Were those days over forever now? Or would the good times come again when Jesus could preach openly without danger from the Pharisees?

She could shut her eyes now and see him, as she had seen him so often — standing in the synagogue, standing in the market place, standing on some grassy hill. She could hear his voice saying the wonderful words:

Do not be anxious for your life, what you shall eat, nor for your body, what you shall put on . . . for your Father knows that you need all these things.

I am the good shepherd. The good shepherd lays down his life for the sheep.

No man can serve two masters.

Had she been trying to serve two masters? Measuring herself by the side of Jesus, she had, or by the side of his mother. She could not think of one without thinking of the other also. People said how much she had changed since she knew Jesus, but his mother had a part in that change, too. Her own ways had grown gentler just watching that other Mary. It was strange they should have the same name!

As she sat now beside the door in the house of Simon the Leper, the dear, sorrowful, joyful memories crowded upon her till she thought she could not bear them. Somehow, she must let Jesus know that she was sorry, that she was grateful, that she would trust and follow him all the days of her life. Somehow, she must pour out herself before him, she who had received so much!

She rose quietly to her feet and slipped out through the half-open door. She paused a moment outside and looked back into the lighted room. No one had moved; no one had seen her go. Jesus was talking earnestly, and the others were leaning **toward** him, listening intently. "My Kingdom," he was saying, "is not of this world." How many times he had told them the same thing! Even the Twelve could not yet quite comprehend; even they were still looking for earthly glory.

The night air felt cool against her cheek as she started down the street. There were loiterers outside the front gate, peering up at the house.

"We want to see Jesus! Is he inside? And Lazarus, the man he raised from the dead?"

Mary Magdalen pretended not to hear. It was just as well not to answer such people. The Pharisees had their spies about, and they might have come as far as Bethany. Mary shivered a little as she hurried toward her house.

When Mary left the home of Simon the Leper, she was not quite sure what she was going to do. But when she reached her own front door she knew. There was a way of telling the Master what was in her heart — a way that would require no words. That was what she needed. She knew she could not trust herself to speak.

She groped her way through the house by the dim light of the little fire burning in the brazier. At the rear of her own small chamber there was a shelf. On that shelf stood an alabaster jar. She felt along the edge of the shelf till she found it. It had stood there for several years. She could remember now the day she bought it at the Jerusalem bazaar. It was displayed with other precious wares from the East — carved boxes of sandalwood, rare brooches of pearls and rubies, small silken scarves. "Mary, how could you!" Martha had exclaimed when she brought it home, for it cost as much as a poor man's yearly wage. She was the old Mary then — the Mary who did not yet know Jesus.

She took it now and started back through the house. The alabaster felt smooth and cool to her touch. She hurried out of the house and down the shadowy street to the house of Simon the Leper. There were more people outside now — after just those few minutes. "Is the Master inside?" they called out. "Is Jesus in there, and Lazarus? We want to see Jesus and Lazarus!" She slipped into the house and closed the door behind her. It was just as well for people not to be peering in — not when there were spies about. Besides, what she was going to do was not for the eyes of strangers.

The Master had stopped speaking, and the group looked about ready to break up for its departure. Peter and John were talking together and Jesus was listening to Simon. Judas was looking about. "He is different from the others," thought Mary, but he was not a Galilean. Perhaps that was the difference. The others seemed more simple and open.

Mary slipped over behind Jesus, and with a quick blow on the edge of the table, broke the top of the jar. In an instant, the room was filled with the pungent sweetness of the finest nard to be found in the Jerusalem bazaar — the most precious perfume anyone could buy. Instantly, all eyes were upon her, but she had no thoughts for anyone but Jesus. Leaning over him, she poured out the contents of the jar on his head, on his feet, tipping it to drain the last drop. It was a courtesy to anoint the head of a guest at supper — but she had poured out a whole pound. A little gasp ran through the room. A pound of that precious stuff? Surely, the Master would rebuke her! The guests broke out into shocked little whispers, but Mary, down on her knees, did not seem to notice. She was drying the feet of Jesus with her hair. He would understand. He would remember a day in Naim, in the house of Simon the Pharisee, when a woman who was sorry for her sins had flung herself at his feet and had anointed them with ointment. That day he had forgiven her; he had given her back her soul. He would forgive her again for those words she had said on the way to the tomb of Lazarus. He would know she was forever grateful.

But Jesus was silent. Had he failed to understand? Judas was speaking instead. He was rebuking her in a hard, cold voice: "To what purpose is this waste? This might have been sold for more than three hundred pieces of silver and given to the poor."

The hot tears scalded their way down Mary's face. They were

right, of course, Judas and the others. They were right and she was wrong — always judging by her heart instead of by her head. And yet — and yet — the Master was not joining with them. He was not rebuking her.

He was starting to speak now, and they were silent, waiting for what he would say. He was not displeased; he was defending her. He did understand, after all . . . "Let her be," he was saying. "Why do you trouble her? She has done me a good turn. She has anointed my body in preparation for burial. Amen, I say to you, wherever in the whole world the gospel is preached, this that she has done shall be told in memory of her."

Mary knelt very still, hardly daring to believe her ears. "Wherever the gospel is preached this shall be told." But one sentence, a sad, mysterious sentence, lay heavy on her heart, chilling it with a strange fear: "She has anointed my body in preparation for burial." No, Lord, no, not that! The perfume which had reached, by now, to every corner of the room, was suddenly sickening in its sweetness. No, not that, Lord.

Simon the Leper's supper had come to an abrupt end. But outside there were voices, many voices. For the crowd had grown immensely in the past few minutes. "Is the Master there," Simon could hear them saying, "the Master who works the miracles?" And some of them were saying, "Is the man there who was four days dead?" Simon could hear the shuffling of many feet.

Simon went to the door and opened it cautiously. "We want to see Jesus and Lazarus," the people called out. Jesus stepped to the door behind his host, and looked out over the upturned faces. There were eager faces — the faces of those who loved him; and curious faces — the faces of those who wanted to see him work some miracle for them; and here and there he saw cold, cruel faces — the faces of those who were plotting to put him to death. He looked at those faces kindly but sadly, then he looked about at the Twelve. He looked very slowly and gently at each one. He was going up to Jerusalem to die for them. How little they understood!

Chapter XX

JESUS ENTERS JERUSALEM
LIKE A KING

ARY the mother of Jesus laid the reins loosely over the neck of her donkey. He was a sure-footed little beast, and they were past the roughest stretch of road. She could afford to rest a little now. Her journey was almost over.

Each year she had come south over those green hills for the feast of the Passover — had come with Joseph, had come with Jesus, had come with neighbors from Nazareth or Capharnaum. Now she was coming with the women who loved Jesus, with Mary of Cleophas, Joanna, and the rest, escorted by the men who loved Jesus, those of the seventy-two who had not come earlier with him. To the rest it was like any other Passover pilgrimage. To Mary it was a thing of sorrow and pain. For she understood. Jesus was going to Jerusalem to die.

It was strange how, even before she knew about the cross, it had cast its shadow — ever since Simeon had looked at her in the Temple with his dim, old eyes and said:

Behold, this Child is destined for the fall and rise of many. . . .
And thy own soul a sword shall pierce. . . .

She had not understood at the time, though she said Yes to God.

She began to understand a little, during the flight into Egypt, and still more, during the three days when she and Joseph had searched for Jesus when he was twelve. She could still hear his boyish voice saying, "Did you not know I must be about my Father's business?" Each year after that she had wondered: When will he be leaving us? When will his mission begin? There had been the day when she watched him out of sight as he left for the Jordan to be baptized by John. "Yes," she said to God that day, "Yes, dear Lord," knowing that she would never have Jesus again in the old way. For this he had been born — to give himself to men. A few weeks later she had watched the men of Nazareth trying to cast him down over the cliff. As the years passed, she had felt the growing hatred of the Pharisees. She had been slowly making her heart ready for this last journey; but it was different when it finally came. Her heart had almost choked her when Jesus said very quietly at their last meeting, "My hour has come." She knew what those words meant.

She had seen little of Jesus in the three years since they left Nazareth. She had seen him less than any of the disciples, less even at times than Joanna of Chusa or Mary Magdalen or Salome. That was the way things had to be. He had said one day to the crowds who followed him: "He who loves father or mother more than me is not worthy of me, and he who loves son and daughter more than me is not worthy of me." How could he say these things unless he and she first gave the example? And yet, though they were not often with each other, they did everything together, he and she. There was not anything they did not share.

Sometimes for weeks at a time he would not come home to the little house in Capharnaum where she lived. Then he would slip in silently, some sweet spring evening when the lemon trees were in bloom, or some winter evening when the wind blew sharply. "Mother," he would say, "I went to Naim. It will be true what you hear — I raised a widow's son to life." Or he would say, "Mother, I am trying to prepare the Twelve for what will happen. I told them today that the Son of Man would be put to death and on the third day he would rise from the dead, but they did not understand. You will have to help them, Mother." Or he would drop down beside her on the bench and say, "Mother, they cannot see that my Kingdom is not of this world. They are still arguing about who will be greatest in it." He had looked very tired that night. She had prayed till the first light of dawn brightened the doorway. Now he was going to die, and she was riding to Jerusalem to help him and his poor little flock. They will be so frightened and bewildered, thought Mary the mother of Jesus as she came near the village of Bethany.

"This must be where Jesus raised Lazarus from the dead," said Joanna of Chusa, as they passed the place of tombs.

"Yes," said Mary softly. But she was thinking of another death. Did no one understand what was going to happen, no one? *Thy kingdom come, thy will be done,* she prayed in the words of Jesus. . . . It was a long journey, a lonely journey, this journey toward the cross.

*   *   *

Up the eastern slope of the Mount of Olives, a crowd moved slowly. Men lined the road, waving green palm and olive branches. They threw down their cloaks before a man riding on an ass. *Hosanna,* they shouted. *Hosanna to the Son of David!* "It's the Master," people cried out to one another, running from their houses to join the crowd. "It's Jesus, the Master!" and they took up the shout:

> Hosanna to the Son of David. . . .
> Blessed is he who comes in the name of the Lord. . . .
> Blessed be the king of Israel. . . .

Just so, many centuries before, another son of David named Solomon had been escorted into the city to be made king. He had been mounted on a mule. . . .

"Will they really make him king?" a little boy called to his father from the side of the road. "Will they make him king of Israel?"

"There's no telling what they'll do, son. There's no telling about a crowd like that."

The people of Bethphage stood in the market square talking, those, that is, who had not joined the crowd and followed Jesus.

"What's that you say, neighbor? It is your donkey he is riding?"

"Yes, my ass, my young foal, with the mother following behind."

"How did that happen, neighbor? Do you know the Master well?"

"It happened in the strangest fashion! Two men came into the courtyard and started untying the colt.

" 'Stop, there!' I shouted. 'What are you doing?'

" 'The Master has need of them,' they answered, and started untying the donkey also. 'He will return them.' It was only then that I recognized they were his disciples. I was a proud man, you may be sure, to see him come riding through the town on my colt, with the people shouting and throwing down their cloaks!"

On up the hill the crowd moved slowly, climbing in a cloud of dust. *Hosanna to the Son of David*, the voices chanted, and branches lay in the road behind to show that the King had passed — the king that was riding on an ass. There was an old prophecy that said:

> Rejoice greatly, O daughter of Zion. . . .
> Behold thy King will come to thee. . . .
> He is humble and riding on an ass,
>   on the foal of an ass. . . .

One more prophecy was being that day fulfilled.

When they reached the top of the hill, the crowd stopped. "What's the matter? What are we stopping for?" some of the people asked, stragglers on the edge of the crowd.

Craning their necks, they saw that Jesus had drawn up his donkey and was looking out over the city. The sight was enough to make anyone draw breath, with the sun gleaming on the great white marble pinnacles of the Temple, the pillars of Herod's palace, and the ramparts of the Roman garrison. Below lay the crowded, crooked streets, with their rows of white-roofed houses. Outside the walls of the city, spread on the grassy slopes of the hillside, were the tents of pilgrims.

It was a beautiful city, a crowded, busy, proud city, but a cruel city. It was a city that would welcome a leader one week and kill him the next. To Jesus, it was a sick city, and he longed with his whole heart to save it. "If thou hadst known in this thy day the things that are for thy peace," he said softly to that city, sitting on his donkey on the crest of the hill. "For days come upon thee when thy enemies will throw up a rampart about thee, and will not leave in thee one stone upon another." He spoke gently, sadly, so that those around him wondered. Some of them would live to see his prophecy come true. Forty years later, enemies would take the city and destroy it. Not one stone of the Temple would remain. The eyes of Jesus were wet as he spoke, but the crowd was becoming impatient. "Hosanna to the Son of David," they chanted.

As they waited on the crest of the hill, they could see another crowd moving toward them. Coming closer, it too caught up the refrain:

> Hosanna to the Son of David. . . .
> Blessed is he who comes in the name of the Lord,
>   the King of Israel. . . .

The two groups met and together they escorted Jesus down the western slope of the hill to the city gate. It was like a triumphal procession.

> Hosanna — hosanna to the son of David. . . .

When they reached the portico of the Temple, the little boys of the Temple school thrust out their heads through the open doors and joined in the cry with their shrill, treble voices:

> Hosanna to the King of Israel. . . .

"Here, what are you doing?" the rabbis called out angrily. "Why are you shouting like that? Come back and recite your passages from the Torah."

"It's the Master, the Galilean!" the little boys cried. "Please, may we go out and see him?"

So that was it! It was the Galilean again! He had come up to the Feast after all, and his followers seemed stronger than ever.

But they would not let him slip through their hands this time!
They nodded to one another behind the backs of the little boys.

"Come back and recite your lessons!" they commanded sharply.
The boys obeyed.

Jesus dismounted from his donkey and went into the Temple.
Once he was inside, the people stopped shouting, and the crowd
gradually scattered. They remembered they had things to do.

Jesus stood in the shadow of a pillar, watching the hurrying men
and women. Jerusalem had welcomed him like a king; but Jerusalem
was not safe. It was full of angry people hatching angry plots,
in spite of the shouting and the palms. He had accomplished his
purpose. He had given them a glimpse of his royalty, in harmony
with an old prophecy. Now he would go back to Bethany for the
night, slipping quietly away through narrow lanes and alleys. The
time had not quite come for him to die for his people — there
was one more thing he must do first. He had promised to give his
disciples a living Bread. When he had done that, he would be
ready to die.

He stood for a moment, watching the people as they went milling
about through the great marble court of the Temple. He watched
them sadly but lovingly. They were his people, and they were
going to reject him; but it was for them that he was going to die.
He watched for a favorable moment to cross the wide court. When
no one was looking, he stepped out from behind the pillar, crossed
the court quickly, and slipped quietly through the gate. In a moment
he was lost in the crowd.

*   *   *

Mary, riding along wearily on the last few miles of her long
journey, wondered at what she saw. There were withered olive
branches and trampled palm leaves scattered along the side of
the road.

"What do you think these dead branches are doing here?" her
companions said to one another.

"Friend, can you tell us what has happened?" they asked a man who was sitting by the roadside.

"What! Don't you know? The Master passed this way coming into the city — the Galilean Jesus! The people threw down their cloaks before him as he rode and waved these branches."

"Was he riding then?"

"He was — on the foal of a donkey."

Mary's heart quickened. She remembered the old prophecy:

> He is humble and riding on an ass,
> on the foal of an ass. . . .

Chapter XXI

JUDAS SELLS HIS MASTER
FOR SILVER

THE High Priest Caiphas rubbed his hands together with satisfaction as he looked about at the distinguished group that was assembling. Priests, Scribes, Pharisees, Elders — they were coming in twos and threes.

"Good day, gentlemen. Will you be seated, gentlemen?"

He had done well to get so many together in broad daylight without attracting the attention of the populace. His house was away from the center of the city, and could be reached by different routes. Besides, people were used to seeing frequent comings and goings at the palace of the High Priest, especially since his father-in-law's house opened out of the same courtyard.

He looked over at his wife's father, Annas, sitting in the place of honor at his right. Annas had been High Priest before him, but had been deposed. He had sharp, piercing eyes that always made his son-in-law uneasy; but now he was glad of the older man's support. This was a tricky business, and difficult. It could only be accomplished by stealth. The Galilean had too great a following for it to be wise to try to capture him by open means. Only this week, he had been escorted into the city like a king. If the authorities didn't watch out, they would have an open rebellion on their hands. It had happened before in Jewish history, and the people were easily inflamed and restless under the restrictions of the Law. But mobs were easily swayed. If he played his cards right, he would have the people with him before he was done. He would have Herod with him too, and Pontius Pilate, the Roman governor. Of course, without Pilate, nothing could be done, for according to present regulations, the death penalty could only be carried out legally by the Roman authorities. Well, he would see to that. Pilate was a timid man. Before the week was out, Jesus would be on his cross, and that would put an end to the business. Once the leader was out of the way, it would not take long for his movement to die. That was the way it was with these popular uprisings!

Of course, the matter would have to come before the Sanhedrin eventually. You had to have the proper court procedures. But in the meantime, it was necessary to plan carefully. He must not escape them again. It was three days since Jesus had made his triumphal entry into Jerusalem. He had showed himself quite openly in the Temple by day, but at night he had gone away to hide. That was what they must find out — where he went each night when he left the Temple; and they must get witnesses against him that would satisfy the Roman authorities.

Looking about, Caiphas raised his hand for silence. "Gentlemen," he began, "about this Galilean, Jesus . . ." They nodded; they understood. He did not need to make a speech to convince them of this thing they were going to try to do. Those who might have objected were not there. He had not invited men like Nicodemus, who had openly defended Jesus the previous autumn, or Joseph of Arimathea, who was showing some signs of sympathy. Only this week Jesus had been most outspoken in his criticism of the Scribes and Pharisees. "Woe to you Scribes and Pharisees," he had said, "hypocrites, because you shut the Kingdom of Heaven against men." He had made other enemies in these past three days, too, for he had driven the venders and money-changers out of the Temple again, the way he had done three years before. The man was certainly helping along his own downfall.

"Gentlemen," said Caiphas, feeling all eyes upon him, "we all feel that this Galilean must be put out of the way. But many of the people are still with him. The questions before us are two: How shall we capture him, when he has so many followers? And on what charges shall we condemn him before the Roman authorities?"

He sat back and waited. Instantly the room was in an uproar. "He blasphemed!" "He stirs up the people!" "He said he will tear down the Temple and build it in three days!" "He breaks the Sabbath by healing men on that day." "He sets up himself as a king." The accusations came from all sides at once.

Caiphas rapped on the table before him. "Gentlemen, may we have order? We all agree that the man deserves death, but we must have witnesses to bring before Pilate. You know how cautious Pilate is, and he does not have our Jewish background. These charges will mean less to him than they do to us."

The room grew somewhat quieter, and one man rose to his feet. "Your Excellency, I will bear witness against the Galilean that he blasphemed. He called himself in my presence the Son of God."

The uproar began again. "We all heard him. He likened himself to God, saying he came down from heaven."

"Gentlemen!" — Caiphas rapped on the table again. "We have one witness. Who will be a second witness?"

Another man jumped to his feet. "I will, Your Excellency. When the people escorted him into the city this week, they called him 'King of Israel,' and he raised no objection."

"Very well, sir. And a third? Have we a third witness?"

And so the meeting proceeded, trumping up flimsy charges against this man, who wanted nothing but to save men's souls — this man who was also God. They rubbed their hands with satisfaction. Pilate should see quite clearly, when they were done, that Jesus was the enemy of Caesar!

"Now, gentlemen," said Caiphas, breathing more easily, "we must consider ways and means of capturing him."

That was harder. It was strange the way he could lose himself in a crowd when he wished. Two or three times they almost had him in their clutches, and he got away, and none knew where he spent his nights. "Somewhere on the Mount of Olives," someone said — but the Mount of Olives had many good hiding places on it. "In Bethany," said another. That was a better clue — they would have Bethany watched. But time was short. As soon as the Feast was over, he would leave, and Jewish law would forbid such procedures against him on the Feast itself or on the Sabbath.

"Gentlemen," said Caiphas nervously, "there is no time to lose." But no one had any very good suggestions to offer.

Suddenly, in the midst of their talk, a door opened, and a servant entered. There was a gentleman at the door, he said, asking for Caiphas.

"Tell him I'm busy. I can't see him," said Caiphas impatiently.

"He insists. He says it's important."

"Who is he? Find out what he wants."

The servant obeyed, and in a minute he was back.

"His name is Judas — Judas Iscariot. He's here about this Jesus."

"Isn't he one of them? I seem to recall the name. Is he a Galilean?"

"Not by speech or dress, Your Excellency."

"Well, show him in."

A general murmur ran through the room now. What could this mean? Was the fellow a spy? Had he been listening to all they had been saying? This might be a ruse, to take up their time and allow the Galilean to get away.

In a moment the man came in, a smooth-mannered, self-assured man, but his hands moved nervously beneath his mantle.

Caiphas regarded him suspiciously. "Your name is Judas, I believe. State your business quickly. We are pressed for time."

"Yes, Your Excellency." He did not speak with a Galilean accent; the servant had been right about that; but perhaps some of the Nazarene's disciples come from other parts.

Judas stood there a moment, uncertainly. He had not expected to see so many faces. He had thought to talk to Caiphas alone, or perhaps with one or two others. It was a bad business to have to do what he was going to do with all those eyes upon him. It was a bad business, but well — it was his chance. He had been deceived about Jesus. He had thought he would be able to rally all Israel about him, and put down once for all the power of Herod and of Rome. His cause was a losing cause. It would be better to get out of it before it collapsed, and to get himself in well with the winning side. And besides, he would need some money to get started again in some line of business. Yes, he had better go through with his plan, once he had begun. But he hadn't thought it would be like this. It was well he had rehearsed what he would say.

"Gentlemen," he said with a slight bow. "I believe you are seeking a clue that might lead to the capture of Jesus."

The eyes focused upon him narrowed. Had he gone too far?

"Never mind what we are seeking," said Caiphas stiffly. "Get on with your business." If the fellow was a spy, he had certainly heard too much. But perhaps he wasn't. After all, it was fairly common knowledge that they were seeking Jesus to destroy him.

Judas bit his lip and hesitated. The speech he had rehearsed wouldn't work. Well, he might as well get it over quickly. "I can deliver him to you, gentlemen. I can deliver him to you tomorrow night. But there will be —" He shifted his eyes uneasily around the room. How should he say it? "There will be a price — a reward, for the information."

He stopped and wet his lips. He looked at the ceiling; he looked down at the floor — anywhere but at those eyes. It was strange how those eyes bored through him. There was satisfaction in their glance, but there was something else in them too. What was it? Disgust — that was it. There was disgust in them! He had not reckoned on that. He thought there would be only satisfaction. He shivered a little. Then he pulled himself together. "Gentlemen, it is to your advantage to accept my offer. How much are you willing to give me?"

They murmured among themselves as he waited. He was picking

with his hands now at the fringes of his mantle. He still could not look at those eyes.

One of the chief priests spoke. "Thirty pieces of silver," he said, as though he were mentioning a figure to start with, expecting that it would be raised.

It was little enough, to be sure, but Judas had lost heart for this bargaining. He wanted nothing so much as to get out of the room. "Thirty pieces will do," he answered.

He waited a minute, shifting his eyes from one face to another, looking for some sign of sympathy. Then looking down again, he blurted out. "He will go tomorrow night to the Garden of Gethsemani. He goes there at night to pray. I will take you to him. The one whom I kiss will be he." He was speaking to Caiphas now, but Caiphas turned away from him and started to speak to his father-in-law.

Caiphas turned back to him coldly. "That is all now. You may go. The rest is a matter for the guard, for the soldiers — not for the rulers of the nation." But nevertheless, there was a glint in his eye. He turned to one of the chief priests. "Will you see that the man gets his money?"

There was the clink of coins being counted. "Here, fellow, take your silver. I will see that you meet the Captain of the Guard."

Caiphas gave a curt nod. Judas, with his hands full of silver but with his face burning, half walked, half stumbled toward the door. He had not thought it would be like this.

Chapter XXII

JESUS GIVES HIS DISCIPLES THE BREAD OF LIFE

 OUNG Jonathan waited his turn at the well to fill his pitcher. Fetching water was woman's work, but Jonathan did not mind. Today was different. Today the Master was coming with the Twelve to eat the Passover Supper, and his mother needed help. At least she thought they were coming, though the Master had not sent word. The mother of Jesus was there, and some of the other Galilean women, and they seemed to expect Jesus. Besides, he often came there for the big feasts.

Jonathan stepped up to the fountain and watched the cold spring water come bubbling into his pitcher. He knew what Jesus would say if he were there. He would say, "I will give you living water. If anyone thirsts let him come to me and drink." Jonathan had heard him say just such words as these at the Feast of Tabernacles. "What did he mean?" Jonathan asked afterward of John, the son of Zebedee, Jesus' disciple. John could often explain things that Jesus said, and John was young. Jonathan did not mind asking him questions. He felt less shy with him than he did with Peter, though Peter was very kind. Peter was older and the chief of the disciples.

Jonathan had not seen Jesus very often — only when he came

up for the big feasts. But he was going to join him as one of his disciples as soon as he was able. "Wait another year, son," his parents had said. "Wait till you are older. The disciples of Jesus never rest. They are always going up and down through the country with no proper place to eat or sleep. Wait a year and then you may go." And so Jonathan was waiting, but he was counting the weeks until he should be able to go. There was no one like Jesus — no one in all the world.

When his pitcher was full, he turned and started down the street toward his house. There were two men walking behind him, conversing in low tones, but he did not look around to see who they were. He was too busy with his own thoughts. It was strange what Jesus said the other day in the Temple. Someone had remarked to him, "Master, look, what wonderful stones and buildings!"

Jesus answered, "There will not be one stone left upon another that will not be thrown down." It was the same day that the Greeks asked Philip to take them to Jesus, and Jesus answered, "The hour has come for the Son of Man to be glorified," and then he added slowly, "I say to you, unless the grain of wheat falls into the ground and dies, it remains alone, but if it dies it brings forth much fruit." He had been silent for a moment, and then he had prayed:

Now is my soul troubled. . . . Father, save me from this hour! No, this is why I came to this hour. Father, glorify thy name.

It was then that the Voice had spoken. Jonathan had not been there; he had not heard the Voice. He would have given everything to hear it! John had told him about it afterward. A Voice from heaven had said very clearly, "I have both glorified it and I will glorify it again."

"I heard it distinctly," John said, "but some people thought it only thundered."

Jonathan was still thinking of these things when he reached his doorstep. He turned a moment before opening the door. There in front of him were the two men who had been following him. They were Peter and John!

"Peter!" he cried full of joy. "John! How did you happen to be following me?"

"That is the strange thing," said Peter. On his face there was a look of wonder and surprise. "You see, it was this way. We were nearing the city when the Master asked us to go and make preparations for the Passover Supper. 'Where are we to eat it?' we asked. All he would tell us was that we were to follow a young man carrying a pitcher of water. 'Into whatever house he enters, there we will eat the supper,' he said. And you were the man!"

They stood silent a moment in front of the house, thinking of this strange thing. How did Jesus know that Jonathan would be coming from the well at just that moment?

"It's not as though I went there every day at this time," said Jonathan. He was less used than the others to the ways of Jesus, but even they were bewildered. They could not help wondering, too, why Jesus had not answered simply, "We will eat it in the Upper Room in Jonathan's father's house." And why, too, had he not sent Judas instead of them? It was Judas who kept the purse, Judas who bought the provisions. Where, in fact, was Judas? He had been away most of the day before, and now again this morning he was absent. At times like this the Twelve usually stayed together. Well, he must be about some business. Doubtless Jesus had sent him on some errand.

"We will go to the Temple for the sacrifice of the Paschal lamb, and you go in and tell your mother to expect the Master," Peter said, after they had finished puzzling about this strange meeting. And so they parted, and Jonathan went into the house.

He set down the pitcher of water. "They've been here," he said, "Peter and John. The Master will be here later with the Twelve." But he did not say how he had come to meet the two disciples.

His mother was spreading the cloth, and Mary the mother of Jesus was cutting up herbs in a wooden bowl — the bitter herbs that the Law prescribed for the Passover meal. The unleavened bread was waiting on the shelf. He stood watching the two of them at their work. Mary looked young to be the mother of Jesus. She turned and smiled at him when he came in, but her eyes were sad. She does not often look that way, thought Jonathan. But when he looked at her again, he did not see the sadness, and he thought, I must have been mistaken. Perhaps it was just the light. He loved to watch her. She was very much like Jesus — as much like him as a woman can be like a man. He himself had the nicest kind of mother, and yet as he watched Mary he could not help thinking, "It would be wonderful to have her for a mother."

His own mother was laying the places at the table now. "That is the place for Jesus," thought Jonathan. "And that is for Peter. And that . . ." Who would be next? Judas or John or Andrew? Probably John, for Jesus was very fond of him; he was so earnest and generous. . . .

"Son," his mother called, breaking into his thoughts, "will you bring up the basin for purifying the hands? And the little towel? You know the ones they use at the Passover Supper."

Of course, how thoughtless of him not to remember! He turned and went out in a hurry. Soon he was back. He loved the hustle and bustle of preparations. This was a wonderful day.

Mary, the mother of Jesus, was pouring vinegar on the herbs, and his mother was pouring out wine from the wineskins into flasks, when there were steps on the stair. "It is Peter and John," thought Jonathan, "back with the lamb." In a moment they were standing in the doorway.

"Did you have to wait long, Peter?" his mother asked.

"No, not long. A good many are not eating the Passover meal until tomorrow night." They spread the lamb out on the table and started preparing it according to the Law. "Thou shalt not break a bone thereof," the Sacred Scriptures said. They bound the legs carefully to a stick.

When the lamb was trussed and ready, Jonathan turned it on a spit over the hot coals. And as he turned the lamb that was made holy to the Lord, he thought to himself: *Tonight, Jesus will come; he will come to eat the Passover with the Twelve — Jesus who is the Son of God.*

*   *   *

The lamps in the lampstands threw flickering lights and shadows over the walls of the Upper Room as Jesus and the Twelve took their places for the Passover Supper. They lit up the table with its white cloth, its platters and cups. They cast a ruddy glow over the faces of the men, over the fine, strong face of Jesus, the big, open faces of Peter and Andrew, the sensitive face of John, the masklike face of Judas. They outlined the basin and pitcher which young Jonathan had placed ready for the purification of the hands.

Jesus stood looking at his followers sadly. They had been in the room only five minutes, and a dispute had broken out among them. He had seated Peter on one side of him, John on the other, with the others ranged in order around the table. It had led to a dispute over which of them should be the greatest. He stood there looking at them, sad at heart. Had he been with them so long, and did they still not understand that in his Kingdom, the least were to be the greatest? Once he had even set a little child in their midst and had told them they must be like that child. "Learn of me," he had said, "for I am meek and humble of heart."

Tonight he would try once more to teach them — in a way they would never forget. He waited till they were seated, and then he rose and went over and wrapped the towel about him which Jonathan had laid out for the purification. He took the basin, poured water into it, and going over, started washing the feet of the disciples. From one to another he went, and they looked at him in amazement, too startled to speak. But when he came to Peter, Peter started up from his place in dismay. He could not let the Master wash his feet! He was only Peter, the fisherman, and Jesus was the Son of the Living God! He could not let him do it!

"Master, you shall never wash my feet," he said quickly.

Jesus looked at him lovingly, but he had a lesson to teach. His voice was stern as he answered: "If I do not wash you, you shall have no part with me."

Peter, in confusion, exclaimed next: "Lord, not my feet only, but also my hands and my head." Poor troubled, impetuous Peter!

"He who has bathed needs only to wash his feet and he is clean all over," said Jesus quietly. Then he looked about at each one, until his eyes rested on Judas. "You are clean," he said, "but not all." A slight flicker passed over the face of Judas. Then Jesus went back to his place. "Do you know what I have done to you? You call me Master and Lord, and you say well, for so I am. If I, the Lord and Master, have washed your feet, you ought to wash the feet of one another. No servant is greater than his master." He waited for the words to sink into their hearts.

But he had not brought them together in that Upper Room to rebuke them. There was another, a dearer reason. There was something he wanted to do for them this night. Yet still the atmosphere in the little group was not right. He looked about again uneasily, and once more his eyes rested on Judas. Then glancing around the room at the upturned faces, he said slowly and sadly: "One of you will betray me."

The disciples looked at one another in dismay, but the face of Judas gave no sign. "Lord, is it I?" they asked, one after another. At first Judas was silent. Then he too asked, "Lord, is it I?"

Jesus turned and said to him very softly, so that only he could hear, "You have said it."

But Peter's uneasiness continued. He could not attract the Master's attention himself, so he whispered across to John, "Ask him who it is."

"Lord, who is it?" John asked, speaking softly to Jesus.

"It is the one to whom I offer this piece of bread dipped in the sauce." Dipping it in, he handed it to Judas.

Judas suddenly got up from the table, and yet he could not have heard what Jesus said.

"What you do, do quickly," Jesus said to him quietly, but Judas did not reply. He went abruptly to the door, opened it, and slipped out without looking back. They could hear his steps on the stairway outside. "He has gone to buy something for Jesus," the other disciples were thinking as they watched him go. The eyes of Jesus followed him very sadly, and rested on the door after he had gone.

The flickering lamps cast long trembling shadows across the floor. Judas was lost by now in the growing darkness. . . . Jesus drew a long, deep breath.

When the footsteps of Judas had died out, Jesus turned again to the group. "Now is the Son of Man glorified," he said, "and God is glorified in him." He looked from one to another very gently. Now that Judas was gone, the moment had arrived — the dearest moment in all his years with them, the moment for giving them the Bread.

More than two years before, he had said to them: "I am the Bread of life. I am the living bread that comes down from heaven. If anyone eats of this bread he shall live forever, and the bread that I will give is my flesh, for the life of the world." Many had been puzzled by those words. Some had gone away and left him because of them. He had not explained at that time, for men's hearts were not yet ready. But now the time had come. Now at last he would give them that Bread, and what he did, others should do after him — on and on until the end of time.

He stood up very quietly, and taking the unleavened bread from the table, he broke it. Eleven small pieces lay on the plate before him. "Take and eat," he said very slowly. "This is my body which shall be given up for you. Do this in remembrance of me." Eleven pieces lay on the plate before him; they looked like bread; they tasted like bread; but they were not bread. They were his own Body. Slowly, solemnly, he passed them to the disciples.

Then Jesus took a cup of wine and mixed a little water in it, as was the custom at the Passover meal. "All of you drink this," he said, "for this is my blood of the new covenant, which shall be shed for you. Do this, as often as you drink it, in remembrance of me." He gave each one the cup to drink.

Then for a moment there was silence. The great truth was making its way into their poor, human minds. Jesus had prepared them for this moment, but it was too wonderful to comprehend all at once. They would not fully understand for some time — not till he sent his Holy Spirit to teach them all things.

Jesus stood watching their faces, lit up by the flickering lamps. They were very much like the faces of children — so simple and unsuspecting. How could he ever prepare them for the trials of this night? Even the Bread was not enough for that — the Bread that was the body of Jesus! Even that would not give them enough strength to bear what was going to happen.

"My little children," he said to them very gently. "Only a little while shall I be with you. You shall seek me, and where I go you cannot come."

They looked at him without understanding. They did not know he was speaking of his death.

"Where are you going?" they asked, and Peter added impulsively, "Why cannot I follow you now? I will lay down my life for you."

Jesus turned and looked at him gently. "Will you lay down your life for me? The cock shall not crow twice before you have denied me three times."

But Jesus did not want to rebuke them now; he wanted to comfort them: "Let not your hearts be troubled. You believe in God; believe also in me. I go to prepare a place for you. I will come again, and I will draw you to myself, that where I am you also may be."

He talked late to them, there in the Upper Room; and the streets outside grew still. There was so much to say before he left them! He must tell them about the Paraclete he would send them, the Holy Spirit, the Comforter.

"I will not leave you orphans," he promised them. But they must live close to him, for their strength would come from him, and without him they could do nothing. "Abide in me and I in you," he said. "I am the Vine, you are the branches. The branch cannot bear fruit of itself unless it live in the Vine." They must live close to each other too. "A new commandment I give to you, that you love one another as I have loved you. By this sign shall all know that you are my disciples, that you love one another."

He said wonderful things, glorious things, consoling things, and the lights went out in the neighbors' houses. But there was something else he had to say to them. Tonight he was going to suffer —

tonight and tomorrow, but later their own turn would be coming
to suffer. He must warn them so they would not be surprised. The
time would come when they would be put out of the Synagogue,
when people would think they had done well to put them to death.
"But have confidence," he said gently. "I have overcome the world."
Then looking up to heaven, he prayed for them.

Father, the hour has come. Glorify thy Son that he may in turn
glorify thee. Not for the world do I pray, but for those whom
thou hast given me, because they are thine. Holy Father, keep in
thy name those whom thou hast given me, that they may be one,
even as we are one.

Yet not only for these do I pray, but for all those who through
their preaching are to believe in me, that all may be one.

The oil had almost burned out in the lamps when he finished
praying. The Passover Supper was over — his beautiful last supper
with them. He rose in his place and the eleven disciples rose with
him. They must sing the final hymn. When the last notes had
echoed from the ceiling, Jesus slowly started toward the door. They
followed him in silence. They did not need to ask him where he
was going. They knew he was going to the Garden of Gethsemani
to pray.

Chapter XXIII

JESUS PRAYS IN THE GARDEN
OF GETHSEMANI

IT WAS good to step out into the cool of the evening. Peter, walking close behind Jesus, took a deep breath. The stars were out and the moon was at the full — the round Paschal moon. The city seemed very quiet, so that their own steps sounded loud against the silence, ringing upon the cobblestones. They walked briskly, and soon they had passed out through the city gate and crossed over the bridge. The gate to the Garden of Gethsemani was just beyond.

Jesus walked along in silence, for the most part, but just before they reached the bridge, he suddenly stopped and said, "You shall be scandalized tonight because of me, for it is written, 'I will smite the shepherd, and the sheep of the flock shall be scattered.' But after I have risen, I will go before you into Galilee."

Peter stepped forward quickly. "Even though all shall be scandalized, I will never be scandalized." Poor, foolish Peter! He had already once been warned: "Amen, I say to you, this night, before the cock crows twice, you will deny me thrice."

Jesus went on again in silence, over the bridge and through the gate of the Garden. Just inside the gate there was a cave where he sometimes left his disciples when he came to pray. He left

161

them there now — all except Peter and James and John. These he took with him. They had seen him in all his splendor on Mount Thabor; now he would have them with him in his hour of need. "My soul is sad unto death," he said to them. "Wait here and watch with me." They had never seen him look so troubled.

The three disciples settled themselves on the ground, under a gnarled old olive tree, and Jesus went farther down the path. It was no new thing for these three to be there; often they had slept under that same tree while Jesus prayed. They sat there now, with the moonlight sifting down through the olive trees, and only the owls to break the stillness. A little distance away, they could see Jesus. He had thrown himself face down upon the path. That was strange — they had never seen him pray that way before.

They had much to think about as they sat, watching the play of light and shadow on the path before them. They thought of Jesus and of how he had washed their feet. They thought of the wonderful Bread which was his body and of the wine which was his blood. They thought of the beautiful prayer which he had prayed for them: "That they may be one even as we are one." Poor Jesus, to be so sad! But as they sat there, thinking of these things, their eyelids grew heavier and heavier. They stirred to try to keep awake, for the sake of Jesus, who wanted them near. They fixed their eyes on the moving branches of the olive trees. It was no use. Slowly their eyes closed. The three dearest disciples were sound asleep.

*   *   *

Jesus, lying face down on the ground, did not see the moonlight or hear the owls. He saw a cross, and he heard the ring of hammers upon nails. He tasted vinegar and gall, and he felt sharp pain through all his body: he was living over in advance tomorrow's agony. His flesh cried out against what he felt and saw. Was there no other way than this for him to save mankind? "Father," he prayed, "if it is possible, let this cup pass from me, yet not my will but thine be done." Over and over he said it in his heart, until gradually he grew quieter. He got up slowly and went over to the three disciples. His heart was sick when he saw they had gone to sleep. But he said gently to Peter, "Simon, do you sleep? Could you not watch one hour?"

The three men stumbled to their feet, sorry and ashamed.

"Watch and pray that you may not enter into temptation," Jesus said, and then, excusing their weakness, "The spirit indeed is willing, but the flesh is weak."

Again he went back and threw himself on the ground. This time he saw all the sins of mankind ever since Adam and Eve committed the very first sin. He saw all the sins of cruelty, the sins of treachery, the sins of idolatry, the sins of anger, the great sins and the small sins, until he felt as though they were weighing him down like a great load which he was not able to carry. They were the sins for which he must atone to his Father in heaven by dying on the cross. The agony of bearing those sins was greater than the agony of the cross. "Father," he prayed again, "if this cup cannot pass away unless I drink it, thy will be done." Then a second time he went over to his disciples, and a second time they were asleep. Then a great loneliness came over him. Was there no one he could count on in his hour of darkness, no one at all? This time he did not rebuke them, and they had no answer to make to him. They were too sick at heart.

A third time he left them and threw himself down on the ground. This time what he saw was still more terrible, for he saw all the sins that were going to be committed down till the end of time. He saw the sins of his enemies, and he saw the sins of those who called themselves his friends. It was hard to say which hurt him more sharply — the big sins of his enemies or the lesser sins of his friends. The sins of the future were harder to bear than the sins of the past, because they made his dying seem in vain. Tomorrow on the cross he was going to win men heaven, and they were going to throw it away. They were going to throw away by their sins all that he earned for them by the cross, the nails, the vinegar and gall. Was it worth doing? Ah, yes, it was worth it if even one soul profited by it — but his soul was sick unto death. He prayed and prayed, and the sweat stood out all over his body, and the sweat was blood. But he clung tightly, with his own will, to the will of his Father, and gradually his body grew quiet. As he lay there on the ground angels came to him to comfort him, and his soul grew peaceful. He no longer wanted the cup to pass. He wanted to drink it.

He got up and went over to the three disciples. They were asleep again, but the tears were on their faces. They were sleeping for sorrow. They stirred as he came to them. "Sleep now and take your rest," he said. But they roused themselves, ashamed. "Behold, the hour is at hand, and the Son of Man will be betrayed into the hands of sinners," he said to them. "Rise, let us go. Behold, he who will betray me is at hand."

They rose stiffly to their feet and came toward him in the moonlight. Even as they did so, they could hear the sounds of marching men. They could see men with torches coming across the bridge.

"Halt! Turn! Wheel! Forward march. . . ."

They could hear the shouted commands. The disciples in the cave heard too and came running toward Jesus.

"Master, there are soldiers coming. They have crossed the bridge and are coming toward the gate. There's a crowd with them!"

While they were still speaking, the procession came clearly into view. They could see the glint of metal in the flickering flames of the torches. Light glanced from the helmets of Roman soldiers and the spears of the Temple police. After them came a rough mob, armed with clubs and cudgels. In front, with the Roman tribune, was a small group of priests and Pharisees.

"Halt," came the ringing command, and the procession stopped just outside the gate.

The disciples drew back a few steps into the shadow of the olive trees, but Jesus did not move. He stood very straight and still in the circle of moonlight, looking toward the gate.

A figure came toward them through the gate. The eleven disciples stared aghast. They knew that walk; even in the dark they knew it. For three years they had known it — in Galilee, in Judea, in the country beyond the Jordan. The man coming toward them was Judas, their friend, the friend of Jesus.

Jesus stood very still, waiting. Nothing in all the world had ever seemed so sad to him as Judas coming across that stretch of grass.

Judas came straight to Jesus. "Hail, Rabbi," he said, and kissed him.

Instantly the mob rushed through the gate and started toward them over the level grass. But Jesus paid no attention to them.

"Friend, for what purpose have you come?" he said very quietly to Judas. "Do you betray the Son of Man with a kiss?"

Then he turned toward the advancing mob. He was ready for what they had come to do. He had already said to his Father in heaven, "Not my will but thine be done."

In a few seconds the crowd had surrounded him. Peter was wide awake now, and trembling with excitement. "Lord," he said, "shall we strike with the sword?" But he did not wait for an answer. Instead, he whipped out his sword from the scabbard and struck out with it blindly. Before anyone realized what had happened, the ear of one of the High Priest's servants lay bleeding on the ground.

Jesus turned toward Peter sternly. "Put back your sword into its place." A shame-faced Peter obeyed. Then Jesus went on more gently: "Shall I not drink the cup that the Father has given me? Do you suppose I cannot entreat my Father and he will even now furnish me with more than twelve legions of angels?"

He reached up and touched the servant's bleeding head. Instantly it was healed. But only those who were nearest knew what had happened.

Turning to the priests, he said, "You have come against me as against a robber. I sat daily with you in the Temple, teaching, and you did not lay hands on me." He paused a minute and then he added very slowly, "This is your hour and the power of darkness." Then he stood still and waited.

The people rushed forward to take him, but suddenly they fell over backward on the ground. Some strange power seemed to be hurling them back. But others came forward and seized him and he made no effort to repulse them, holding up his hands to be bound. He was following the will of his Father, like a lamb led to the slaughter. The cold chains bit into the white wrists of Jesus. Someone pushed him forward into the mob.

"Attention. About face. Forward march." The little procession formed again, and started back toward the gate of the Garden. But now, there was scarcely any order left. People were scoffing, shoving, cursing. They were spitting at Jesus, mocking him, striking him. Out the gate they went and over the bridge, in the light of the flaring torches.

Back under the shadow of the olive trees, the eleven disciples were hiding — trembling in fear for their lives. The prediction of the prophets had come true:

I will smite the shepherd and the sheep of the flock will be scattered.

Not one of them had dared to go with Jesus.

Chapter XXIV

PETER DENIES HIS LORD

ETER and John, crouching among the olive trees, shivered as they stared into the dark. It seemed twice as dark, now that the torches were gone. They could hear the cries growing fainter and fainter, moving across the bridge. When the sounds had finally disappeared, they crept out and looked about. They did not see the others, for all of them had run in different directions when the mob had come forward to bind Jesus. They stood a moment, too shaken to speak or think. Then they started off stealthily toward the gate. There was really no need of stealth, for the crowd was gone. Besides, the mob had taken their prize. They were not interested in a handful of frightened fishermen. "Let them go," one of the priests had said, as the disciples had started to run away. "We have the one we want."

Once out of the gate, they headed for the bridge, and on up through the crooked streets toward Jonathan's house. They had no clearly thought-out plan, but they would stop there first. They would stop there to see the mother of Jesus. . . .

They found her by a window on her knees.

They burst into the room excitedly and then stopped. She was kneeling very still, but they could see she had been weeping. They started to back out again, but she turned around, and rose to her feet. They had rehearsed in their thoughts how to tell her, but now they blurted it out, just as it came.

"They have taken him, Mary. We don't know where, but we think to the house of Caiphas. He knew it was going to happen. He prayed till the blood ran down his face, and we slept, Mary, when he needed us. It was Judas who betrayed him, Mary, with a kiss. When they bound him, we ran away. We ran from Jesus. . . ."

They had always known Mary was different from other women, but they never knew how different till she stood there quietly before them, listening to them in the moonlight. Her face was full of pity as she listened — pity for them, for the ones who had run away from Jesus!

They left her, a little while later, quieted and strengthened. They left her to try to find Jesus.

They started up through deserted streets toward the house of Caiphas, but as they drew nearer, they began to see hooded forms moving stealthily along in the shadows. For in the time since the capture of Jesus, messengers had been hurrying through the streets in the upper part of town, knocking cautiously on doors.

"Hist, they have him," they had whispered at each house. "They've caught the Nazarene. The Sanhedrin is meeting tonight in the house of Caiphas. Come as soon as you can."

"Hush, did you hear the news? They have Jesus! They caught him tonight! The Sanhedrin is meeting. . . ."

"The Sanhedrin is meeting tonight. Come quickly. . . ."

Soon many sandaled feet were shuffling through dark streets, all in the same direction.

When John and Peter reached the house of Caiphas, they slipped into a doorway and watched. One by one, the figures stole up to the gate and knocked. Softly the door opened; softly the figures slipped inside; softly the door closed. Something was happening in the house of Caiphas — something that men wanted to hide.

When the street was empty, Peter and John crossed over, and stood a moment outside the gate. Their fear was returning — the cold, paralyzing fear that Mary for the moment had driven away. Finally Peter got up courage to knock. There was no answer. He knocked again — more loudly. Then the door opened, and a serving maid put out her head. She stared at their rough clothes and their country faces.

"What do you want at this hour?" she asked abruptly.

"We want to come in," said Peter. "We have business."

"You have business, have you? At the house of the High Priest, in the middle of the night! Go on with you!" She shut the door in their faces.

But John knew someone in the High Priest's household. "Shall I try?" he asked Peter, and Peter nodded. John knocked and again the maid put out her head. She was about to shut the door, when he whispered something in her ear. Her manner changed ever so slightly.

"All right, if you've a mind to — come in." But she eyed them suspiciously as she led them inside and pushed the big door shut behind them.

They were in a large open court that joined the house of Caiphas with that of his father-in-law, Annas. In the center a fire was burning, and a group of servants and guards were gathered around it, warming their hands.

"They've got him," one of them was saying. "They've been laying for him for days. One of his own men betrayed him."

Peter, coming toward the fire, winced as he listened.

"Where is he now?"

"Annas has him — just till the Sanhedrin is ready for him. The man has courage! You should have heard how he answered Annas — without any fear at all. One of the guards struck him."

John was very pale as he listened, but Peter could feel his blood mounting to his forehead. The group around the fire seemed to have forgotten them; but suddenly, in a lull in the conversation, the serving maid swung around and stared at them.

"This man was with him," she said, pointing to Peter. She arched her eyebrows as she spoke. "You are one of this man's disciples."

Peter's heart pounded and his mouth felt dry, as all eyes turned toward him. "Woman, I do not know him," he answered quickly, hardly knowing what he said.

He slipped out of the circle of light, but the maid followed him curiously.

"You are one of them," she repeated.

Peter turned back, trapped. "I am not," he said shortly, with an oath. His thoughts now were in a whirl. Far away, outside the walls of the city, a cock crowed faintly, but he barely heard. He turned back again to the fire; it seemed no use to try to get away.

For a time after that no one spoke to him. They were busy wondering what was going on inside. Then someone turned to him again. "Surely you are one of them. Even your speech betrays you. Didn't I see you with him in the Garden?" It was a kinsman of Malchus, whose ear Peter had struck off.

Peter's fear mounted, and again he denied it with an oath. Just then a cock crowed a second time. Suddenly, Peter's heart stood still. What had he been saying? He could hear the Master's voice, "Before the cock crows twice, you will deny me thrice."

Just then a door opened and there was the tramp of feet, the rattle of chains. Jesus was being led across the courtyard. His face was streaked with blood, and his clothes were torn and stained. He was being jostled along between guards; but just a moment, as he passed, he turned and looked at Peter. In his face there was sorrow and pain, but more than these there was love, and the love pierced the heart of Peter. With a rush, the sharp tears stung his eyes. He slipped out of the group and over to the door, which opened as he pushed it. In a moment he was in the street outside. He leaned up against a wall, and let the hot tears come, the sharp, cleansing tears of sorrow. They were sweet tears too, healing tears. For in that swift, fleeting glance of Jesus, he knew he had been forgiven.

*   *   *

Jesus was led into the great hall in the house of Caiphas. Looking about quietly he could see, through his bloodshot eyes, row on row of faces, ranged before him. He could see by the flaring lamps in the great bronze lampstands that they were proud, angular faces, all ugly with hate. Caiphas sat before him in a broad, carved chair, with his father-in-law beside him. There was satisfaction in the small, shifty eyes of the High Priest as he looked at his victim. His plans had worked well thus far, and his witnesses were all primed. Conviction should come quickly. He looked over at Annas and nodded. Yes, he was well pleased.

Jesus, standing before Caiphas, looked into his soul and was sad. It was a warped, twisted, deformed soul, and yet God had made it. He had made all the souls in that room, yet now they were all ugly and rotten with envy and hatred and cruelty. Jesus had come to save those souls, and now they were rejecting his gifts. That thought hurt more than the hard iron chains that bit into his wrists, more than the bruises on his face. "Father, forgive them," he prayed to himself, as he looked into the faces before him.

"Gentlemen," said Caiphas, looking about at the rows of men before him, "shall we proceed to the examination of the prisoner? What are your accusations?"

And so, the tragic farce began.

"He says he will make himself king."

"He heals men on the Sabbath."

"He says he will destroy the Temple and in three days rebuild it."

They were the charges they had rehearsed, and yet, as they went on talking, these men with the narrow, jealous faces, they began to contradict themselves, and their stories, one with another, did not agree. Caiphas began to look anxious; his small eyes narrowed still further in anger. Couldn't these fellows remember their parts even one day? They would never make their case convincing when they came before Pilate! Well, he would have to take matters into his own hands. Perhaps, by questioning, he could get the prisoner to convict himself. . . . He held up his hand for silence and turned toward Jesus.

For a moment the two men faced each other — the man that was so much less than a man, in spite of his priestly robes, and the

Man that was so much more than a man, even in his torn garments. For a moment, it was Caiphas who was on trial before Jesus, though Caiphas did not know it. As yet, Jesus had not spoken. His business was with the truth, not with lies. When he could bear witness to the truth, he would speak.

Caiphas leaned forward and wagged his long finger. He knew he was about to play a winning card. "I adjure you by the living God that you tell us whether you are the Christ, the Son of God."

"I am," Jesus answered quietly. This was the truth he had come into the world to teach. He was silent a moment, and then his face lighted up with a wonderful inner fire. "And you shall see the Son of Man sitting at the right hand of the Power and coming with the clouds of heaven," he said, carried along, for a moment, in the glory of the vision. Then he was silent again. He had borne witness to the truth.

A look of triumph came into the face of Caiphas. This was better than he had dared to hope. He shut his eyes as though outraged at the words, and tore his mantle, as a pious Jew does when he hears the name of God blasphemed. Then he stood up and called out loudly: "What further need have we of witnesses? You have heard the blasphemy. What do you think?"

On every side, men jumped to their feet and shouted: "He blasphemed! He is worthy of death! Let the Nazarene die!" They too tore their garments.

The guards rushed toward him and struck him. They mocked and spat at him. One of them blindfolded him, and striking him, called out, "Prophesy to us, O Christ, who struck thee." Jesus did not answer. *Father, forgive them,* he was praying.

But now it was growing late. The lamps were flickering and burning low. Men were beginning to think of bed.

"Let the prisoner be led out," Caiphas commanded, and the soldiers, wearying of their sport, led him out to be locked up for the night. It would not be a very long night; half of it was already gone. He would spend what was left of it in praying. It would be hard to pray upon the cross.

Chapter XXV

JESUS IS CONDEMNED TO DEATH

ONTIUS PILATE climbed the platform in the square before the praetorium and looked out over the sea of angry faces. It was the third time that morning he had mounted that tribune, and each time the mob had been larger and uglier. He stood there a moment with a most uneasy mind.

He hated these Jewish holidays. There was almost always some kind of trouble — riots, robberies. There was no telling what would happen. He had been aware lately of a growing feeling about the Nazarene called Jesus, but he had thought at first it was just some small religious squabble. These Jews went crazy over their religion! The Emperor Tiberius had warned him to humor them in such matters. That was why he had given permission for the cohort of soldiers to arrest the Galilean leader when the request came from the High Priest. Yet somehow, he was uneasy.

The man did not look like a criminal. In fact, Pilate could not help wondering how anyone could stand there so quietly when he was on trial for his life. There weren't many soldiers in the Imperial Legions that had such courage. As for the accusations against him — the witnesses could not even agree. They accused him of wanting to make himself king, but it was just his way of speaking of his religious program. What was the phrase he used? 'My Kingdom

173

is not of this world.' It was just envy that was prompting the chief priests. Too many people were running after him! It was plain the man was innocent. "I find no guilt in this man," he had already said to the crowd.

But the people had persisted. "He is stirring up the people, teaching all through Judea and Galilee." He seized on the word Galilee. Herod, the Tetrarch of Galilee, was now living in Jerusalem. He would send the Galilean to him. Herod could decide! And so the pitiful little procession had moved off through the streets to Herod's palace, with the crowd jeering behind it. But Jesus had refused to speak to Herod. He had remained silent through all his questioning. He had no words for the man who had killed John the Baptist at the whim of a dancing girl, and who had killed half the members of his own family.

"What happened?" Pilate asked the officer who commanded the guards.

"The Nazarene refused to speak."

"And Herod?"

"He was angry. He let his servants make sport of him. They dressed him in a white cloak and mocked him."

"And the Nazarene, did he still keep silence?"

"Yes, Your Excellency."

Well, that plan had failed. He was again faced with the problem of appeasing the people. He looked out over the seething mob of faces — cold, cruel faces, eager for their prey. But the Man's eyes haunted him as he sat in the judgment seat, stalling for time. They were quiet, kind eyes, and they seemed to be searching and measuring him. Sometimes they even seemed to be sorry for him. It was a fanciful thought, of course! At any rate, he would like to save him if he could. At the time of the Feast he always released one prisoner, in accordance with the Roman custom. He always let the people choose their man. It was a faint hope that they might let him release the Galilean, but he would try.

He called out in a loud voice. "Whom shall I release to you, Barabbas, or Jesus, who is called Christ?"

"Barabbas!" they cried, "Barabbas!" It made him shiver to hear them, for Barabbas was a very evil man, guilty of many crimes.

As he sat looking out over their angry faces, he saw a messenger coming toward him, pushing his way through the crowd. The man handed him a tablet on which was written: "Have nothing to do with that just man; for I have suffered many things in a dream because of him." The message was signed with his wife's seal.

He turned suddenly cold as he read it. His wife was a wise and prudent woman, and besides, you could not quite tell about dreams. Julius Caesar's wife had been warned in a dream just before he was slain. . . .

He would do what he could to save the prisoner. He called out again to the crowd, "Why, what evil has this man done? I find no crime deserving death in him. I will chastise him and release him."

"Crucify him!" they cried. "Crucify him!"

Pilate turned and climbed down from the tribune, but he thought, I will chastise him anyway. Perhaps when they see him they will be satisfied.

"Chastise the prisoner," he ordered the officer of the guard.

Jesus, bound to the pillar, tried to fix his thoughts on the loving will of his Father, as the sharp scourges bit into his flesh. He tried to remember the souls who were waiting to be saved by his love. He tried, but his mind kept drifting into darkness. His body, when the soldiers finished, felt as though it were wrapped in fire. "Not my will but thine be done," he prayed, as his mind grew clearer.

But the soldiers had not finished with him. Men said he pretended to be a king. Very well, they would make him a king! One soldier took thorn branches and, twisting them into a crown, pressed it down on his head. Another found a purple cloak to put on him. A third thrust a reed into his hand.

"Hail, King of the Jews!" they cried, and they struck and spat at him.

When they had finished with their sport, they took off the cloak, and put his own torn, bloodstained one back on, and led him, in his crown of thorns, to Pilate. When Pilate saw him, even he was shocked, though he had seen many such sights in his day. Surely, if the people see him now, they will be satisfied, he thought. And so, for the fourth time, he went outside and mounted the tribune, but this time he brought Jesus with him. Putting Jesus in front of him, he called out: "Behold the man! I bring him out to you that you may know I find no guilt."

But his plan did not work. The people, seeing Jesus, only cried the harder, "Crucify him!"

"Crucify him yourselves, for I find no guilt in him!" he called out to them, exasperated, knowing full well that they could not do it; for only he had the power.

One of the chief priests spoke up. "We have a Law, and according to that Law, he must die, because he has made himself the Son of God."

Something about those words struck fear into his already anxious mind. He went into the praetorium again and asked Jesus, "Where are you from?"

Jesus did not answer. He was peering sadly into the soul of this man before him, this man who was not altogether bad, but weak.

Pilate was not used to being answered with silence. "Do you not speak to me?" he asked, somewhat impatiently, and yet he marveled, too. "Do you not know that I have the power to crucify you and to release you?"

"You would have no power at all over me," Jesus answered quietly, "if it were not given you from above. He who betrayed me to you has the greater sin."

Pilate stood a moment, staring at Jesus, bewildered by the answer. Then he went back to the tribune. He must put an end to this matter; it had been dragging on all morning. But he still hoped for some way of saving this man with his kind eyes and amazing self-possession.

But in the meantime, the chief priests had been thinking of another argument — one that would silence Pilate once for all. For they had guessed correctly his hidden weakness.

"If you release this man, you are no friend of Caesar!" they cried out to him, with triumph in their eyes. "Everyone who makes himself king sets himself against Caesar."

If there was any man in all the world whom Pontius Pilate feared, it was Tiberius Caesar. He had already aroused Caesar's anger once since he had been in Judea by his handling of the Jews. If there was an uprising now, there was no knowing what Caesar would do!

Slowly but surely, Pilate was slipping into their power. They could see he was yielding. But he brought forward Jesus once more. "Behold your King!" he said to them. There was no softening them now!

"Away with him! Away with him!" they shouted.

"Shall I crucify your king?"

"Crucify him!" they answered. "We have no king but Caesar."

With a strong distaste for the thing he was about to do, he seated himself in the judgment seat and called for a basin of water. When it was brought, he washed his hands slowly, deliberately, in the sight of all the people.

"I am innocent of the blood of this just man," he said. "See to it yourselves."

"His blood be on us and on our children," the crowd answered.

And so, he released to them Barabbas, and pronouncing sentence, delivered up Jesus to be crucified.

Once the sentence was passed, matters moved quickly. There were sharply shouted orders:

"Bring out the other condemned prisoners!" There were two others awaiting execution — two thieves.

"Let the crosses be brought!" They were brought forward by the soldiers.

"Transcribe the cause of condemnation!" The boards were brought, and the paint and brushes.

"What shall we write for the Nazarene, Your Excellency?"

Pilate thought for a moment. Then a glint came into his eye. "Write *Jesus of Nazareth, King of the Jews.*"

It was painted in black letters on the white board — in Latin, Greek, and Hebrew.

The chief priests and Pharisees, craning their necks to see, cried out in anger. "Write not, 'The King of the Jews.' Write, 'He said, I am the king of the Jews.'"

But Pilate saw it as a way to annoy the chief priests. "What I have written I have written," he said, and he would say no more.

Chapter XXVI

JESUS DIES ON THE CROSS

I'M GOING to the city today," Simon of Cyrene said to his sons Rufus and Alexander. "I'll be back before dark." He was still called Simon of Cyrene, although he had been living in the neighborhood of Jerusalem for some time.

"Watch out. There's been some trouble in the city. I heard from a merchant who was traveling this way that they've taken the Nazarene."

"I'll be careful, never fear." Simon smiled as he put on his cloak. "Nobody will bother an old fellow like me." He folded his cloak about him with his caloused hands. He was a tall giant of a man, despite his sixty years.

As he threaded his way along toward the ramparts of the city, he noticed that the roads were unusually crowded, but that was not surprising at the time of the Passover. But when he entered the city, up near the praetorium, he began to hear shouts and cries. At first he heard only a confused murmur, but as he got closer, he could pick out words: "Crucify him! Crucify the King of the Jews!" "Save yourself if you are a king!"

As he turned the corner near the guardhouse, he found himself suddenly caught up in a shoving, shouting mob that was moving along slowly from the praetorium. Over the din he could just hear the clatter of horses' hooves and the clanking of swords on armor.

"Get out of there, fellow," someone shouted at him. "Can't you see that centurion coming? Get out of the way of the prisoners."

He stepped back, bewildered.

"There, you great country fellow. Don't you know what is happening?"

Caught now by the crowd that was pressing against him, he looked in the direction of the sounds. There was a mounted centurion, leading foot soldiers, with three prisoners carrying crosses. Two of them were great, brawny fellows, who were cursing and swearing under their heavy loads. But the third one was different. He was slender and silent, with great dark eyes — sad, swollen, and yet wonderful eyes. His load seemed too heavy for his shoulders; he was staggering under it. Then, just as Simon was looking, he fell, and it took two soldiers to get him back on his feet again. It was plain that he was not like the others. Simon was craning his neck to see the inscription on the cross, when suddenly he felt a heavy hand on his shoulder.

"Here, fellow," a sharp voice shouted in his ear, "you look like a stout fellow. This man can't carry his cross. You fall in behind and carry it for him."

He looked about to see a black-faced soldier grinning up at him.

At that moment he wanted nothing so much as to be back in the vineyards on his hillside. But there was nothing else to do. Simon stepped forward and picked up the prisoner's cross. As he did so, he could read the inscription: *Jesus of Nazareth, King of the Jews.* So this was the Jesus men had talked so much about! Could it be he was an imposter, after all?

Simon moved along with the three prisoners, and soon he too began to receive the taunts and jeers of the crowd. He wanted to curse and shout back, but something stopped him, something he could not explain — something that was bound up with the pitiful, patient silence of that man who stumbled along ahead of him. It was a wonderful silence. "Wonderful," he said afterward to Rufus and Alexander, struggling to express what he could not put into words. "I cannot tell you why I felt that way, but he was wonderful — and so was she. . . ."

He had known the minute he saw her that she was his mother. Other women had spoken to him — women who wept and pleaded. One had darted out and wiped his face with her scarf before the soldiers could stop her. Others sent up such piteous cries that he stopped to comfort them. "Weep not for me but for yourselves," he had said, "and for your children." Other things he had said too, which Simon could not understand, but he understood the wonderful kindness. "And he was going to his death!" he exclaimed to Rufus and Alexander. "He was kind, going to his death!"

But *she* — the woman who must have been his mother — was different. She did not weep aloud, or plead with him, or cling to his garments, or wring her hands, as other women would. No, she too was silent. But when he came opposite her, the most wonderful look passed between them. "As though this was something they were doing together," Simon explained afterward in his house to Rufus and Alexander. "And to think," Simon said to his sons, "to think that I almost cursed my fate when they asked me to carry his cross! Sons, we are just to late. We just missed the most wonderful thing. We just missed being his disciples!"

*   *   *

Mary was carried along by the crowd through the narrow, dark streets of Jerusalem. At times she could see Jesus; at times he was hidden from her view. "He is doing this for love," she kept saying over and over to herself. "We are doing it together for love." What was the phrase of Jesus? *"That they might have life and have it abundantly."* That was why they were doing it.

She tried hard to keep those words in her mind as she was jostled and elbowed by the crowd. And she tried, too, not to hear the things they were saying.

"He called himself the King of the Jews, did he? What kind of king is he now?"

"The son of a carpenter called himself a king!"

She tried not to hear.

"That one won't last long," someone said behind her, as Jesus fell for the second time. "See, he's all faint already."

"Hush, that's his mother!"

"Is she? She looks young."

"Hush, she'll hear you. Suppose it was your son!"

"He called himself the Son of God, didn't he? The priests say that's blasphemy."

"Hush, he healed old Jacob."

Mary tried to blot out their talk from her mind. She must keep her thoughts on the will of the Father. "Thy kingdom come; Thy will be done . . . " she prayed. It was good to be able to pray in the words of Jesus. She could hear his voice saying, "For God so loved the world that he gave his only-begotten Son. . . ." How little men understood!

The crowd pushed out through the city gate and up the slope of the hill. When they reached the top, the centurion called "Halt!" "This place will do," he said, wiping his face with a handkerchief. "Get back there. Make the crowd move farther back!"

The people stepped back, shoving and jostling. Then they stood very still, for the soldiers were getting ready to nail the hands of Jesus — the beautiful, kind hands that had healed so many.

Mary took a quick step backward. She was very pale.

"What's the matter, lady?" someone said kindly. "Are you sick?"

Mary shook her head. She could not trust herself to speak. She braced herself for what was coming. The soldiers started pounding the long nails, and each blow of the hammer sent a sharp pain through her. "But it is a blow of love," she thought. She knew it was that to Jesus — each blow a blow of love.

At last the hammering stopped and she breathed a little easier. But then they started raising the cross. "Lift it up!" the centurion ordered. "Up farther. It's not straight yet. A little more to the right. There!" The heavy cross settled into its hole. Mary could feel the pain of it quivering through her. Everything he felt she felt too. She could understand now, as never before, the words of

Simeon: "And thy own soul a sword shall pierce." She could understand too more clearly the words of Jesus: "I, when I am lifted up, will draw all men unto me. . . ." When one of the soldiers reached up to him a cup of wine and myrrh, he tasted it and shook his head. She understood. It would dull the pain, and he wanted to feel it. It was part of his gift to the Father. She stood very still as she watched. The hot tears stung her eyes but she held them back. She must hold them back for Jesus! They were doing this thing for love.

Jesus looked down from his cross at the soldiers who were catching their breath after their heavy work. A look of compassion came into his poor, bruised face. They were not to blame! They were only doing their work. *"Father, forgive them,"* he said, *"for they know not what they do."*

The soldiers picked up their tools and went over to the two thieves. They were not quiet like Jesus. They cried and cursed — poor frightened human creatures! When the soldiers had finished with them, they threw themselves down on the ground to rest. It had been hard work, just as the sun was hottest. It was cooler now, ominously cooler, the way it is when the sun goes under a cloud. They looked at the sky — but there were no clouds.

Others looked about too. "What's this!" they exclaimed. "It's getting dark and it's only just noon! There aren't any clouds!"

They blinked and stared. "It's some strange wonder in the sky!"

"Do you think it's a judgment on the Jews?"

"Tush! Nonsense! Don't let the Pharisees hear you!"

The enemies of Jesus appeared not to notice. They stood in groups, jeering and mocking. "He saved others! Let him save himself!" "If he is the Christ, let him come down from his cross!"

The two thieves joined in the mocking: "If you are the Christ, save yourself and us."

Jesus hung silent. The soldiers took out dice and started gambling to pass the time — gambling for the clothes of Jesus.

"Save yourself and us!" repeated one of the thieves, shouting and cursing. But the other one did not shout. He had started wondering. Who was this man who was silent when men cursed him, who prayed for his executioners? He twisted painfully around and looked at Jesus. Then he turned back to the other thief with a groan of pain. "Don't you even fear God," he said to the other, "you who are under the same sentence? We are receiving what our sins deserve, but this man has done no wrong." He turned back again toward Jesus and studied his face. It was a wonderful face, even now when it was bruised and bleeding. Suddenly he was filled with longing. Looking at that face, he wanted to be clean and good again, the way he had been as a child. He wanted to be rid of his sins.

"Lord," he said to Jesus, groping for words, "remember me when you come into your kingdom."

Jesus turned painfully and looked at him. "Amen, I say to you," he said very gently, "this day you shall be with me in paradise." He sank back, exhausted with the effort.

The crowd was dwindling now, and Mary was able to move forward nearer to Jesus, with John and Mary Magdalen and some of the other women. As she moved, Jesus opened his eyes and looked about as though searching for someone. His eyes rested on her and his face lit up. Then he shifted his glance to John, then back to Mary.

"Woman," he said very gently, "behold your son," and to John, "Behold your mother." Then he shut his eyes again, as though wearied by too great effort. He did not speak again for nearly three hours. They were slow, hard hours.

Mary kept her eyes fixed on Jesus, watching for each slightest change. He made no move, but the look of pain deepened on his face. She could see he was growing weaker. Then suddenly he raised his head. He moved his parched lips as though trying to speak. Then, with great effort he cried out: "My God, my God, why hast thou forsaken me?"

For a moment Mary's heart stood still. Was he in so much darkness? Then she understood. That was not a cry! It was a prayer! It was the opening verse of one of the Psalms of David. She could still hear old Anna chanting it to her in the Temple. "That psalm is a prophecy," Anna had said. "It tells of the death of the Messias. Israel has always slain its prophets . . . " and she had sighed and gone on with her spinning. Today that prophecy was being fulfilled. Perhaps that was what he was trying to say. Why didn't men see they were slaying the Son of God!

He was silent a few minutes. Then he started moving his head from side to side. "*I thirst*," he said with difficulty. One of the soldiers dipped a sponge in vinegar and moistened his parched lips. His eyes were glazed and sightless now, but he lifted them up to heaven. "*It is consummated*," he said in a strong, clear voice. His whole body shook; then he called out loudly, "*Father, into thy hands I commend my spirit*." His head dropped forward. He was dead.

No sooner had he died than the whole earth began to quake. The earthquake made great cracks in the rocky hillside. It split open the tombs and the dead came out and walked. In the Temple, the priests came running out in fear, for the great veil in the Holy of Holies was torn from top to bottom. Everywhere, people ran about in terror, beating their breasts.

Mary stood very still before the cross of Jesus, praying. His work of dying was done — his work of love. He would go on working, but in a different way. Her work — the work he had given her that day — had just begun. She was to be the mother, not of John only, but of all the world. She understood.

Suddenly, as she stood praying, a frightened centurion ran toward her — the centurion who had crucified Jesus. He was shaking from head to foot, but on his face there was a sudden look of wonder. "Truly," he said to her in a strange, hushed voice, "this was a just man. Truly this was the Son of God!"

Chapter XXVII

JESUS IS LAID IN THE TOMB

C LOVES, spices, herbs for the Passover! Everything for the Passover!"

Nicodemus pushed through the crowded market square with a heavy heart. People brushed past him, women with baskets, little boys with leather pouches, servants with wineskins. Everyone else was intent on the Feast.

"Penny, sir, penny for a poor, blind beggar."

Nicodemus reached down into his wallet and brought out a penny. If Jesus were here, he would touch those poor, sightless eyes, and the man would see. If Jesus were here! But Jesus was stretched on a cross on a hill called Calvary. Jesus was dead.

Nicodemus stepped into a shop. "Do you sell spices here? Spices for burial?"

"Yes, sir. Myrrh and aloes, sir. May I console you in your loss, sir. Is it a relation? A father, perhaps? A brother?"

Nicodemus hesitated a moment. "No, a friend — a very dear friend."

So much more than a friend, he thought to himself. So much more than a brother or father! If he had only understood better, before Jesus was dead! He could hear the centurion's frightened words: "Surely this was the Son of God!" And to think that he,

Nicodemus, had had the chance to follow him almost from the very start! He could still see Jesus silhouetted in an open doorway in the flickering light of a lantern, saying: "No one shall see the kingdom of God unless he be born again." Now at last he had been born again — too late.

"I see, sir," said the seller of spices. "You are a generous man to be burying your friend. How much do you wish to buy?"

With a sudden rush of tears to his eyes, Nicodemus stammered out, "A hundred pounds. I'll take a hundred pounds."

"A hundred pounds, sir! That is a great deal. We sell that much only for chief priests and rulers of the people."

"He was a ruler," Nicodemus said softly — too softly for the man to hear. He could hear Jesus saying to Pilate, "My kingdom is not of this world." Was it only this morning he said it? It seemed to belong to another life. The man had his back turned, weighing out the spices. Nicodemus was glad, for the tears came faster now than he could wipe them away.

Presently the man turned around. "How will you take them, sir?"

"I will send my servant," Nicodemus answered, counting out the money. "He will be here presently."

"Thank you," said the man. "If I may be so bold, they sell linens in the next street — burial linens. I thought you might like to know. Good day to you, sir. The blessing of God be on you."

Nicodemus did not go to the seller of linens. Joseph of Arimathea was taking care of that, and of getting the permission from Pilate for the body of Jesus. The dear, precious body . . . Joseph owned a tomb near the place where the crosses stood, and he was offering his tomb for Jesus. He had just had it made, and it had never yet been used.

Somehow, one could not think of putting Jesus into anything but a new tomb.

Nicodemus threaded his way home, but all along the route he could hear people talking. "Did you feel the earthquake? They say the graves opened and the dead came out!" "Did you know that the great veil in the Temple has torn in two?" "It's a judgment of God. Do you think it can be because they killed the Nazarene?" Nicodemus did not stop till he reached his house. He dispatched his servant for the spices and then hurried off toward Calvary. The mother of Jesus would be waiting with the tall young fisherman named John. He could not think of her, standing three hours by the cross of Jesus, without thinking of the passage of Scripture: "Who shall find a valiant woman? Far and from the uttermost coasts is the price of her." Yes, she was valiant — as valiant as her Son. Even after Jesus had died, she stood beside him praying, until the fisherman John had spread down his cloak and made her rest on it. Only then had the tears come — the sharp, sweet tears of loving sorrow. She would still be there waiting for him and Joseph to come. He must hurry back to her.

Joseph of Arimathea stopped at a shop in the street of the weavers to buy burial linens for Jesus, and then hurried through the streets toward the praetorium. Everywhere the people were talking excitedly. "The great veil in the Holy of Holies is torn." But Joseph hurried on. He could not stop to talk or he would be too late, for they would be taking Jesus down from the cross before sunset. Tomorrow was the Sabbath, and they would have to do it before the Sabbath rest began.

He mounted the stone steps of the praetorium. "May I see the governor?" he asked. Joseph was a member of the Sanhedrin; he spoke with authority. The guard looked him up and down, and went strolling off toward the audience chamber.

"Your Excellency, there is a Jew outside who wants to see you. He seems a man of importance."

Pilate sighed. "Let him come in," he said. He was wondering to himself if the day would never end.

Joseph came forward hestitantly. He did not know how Pilate would respond.

"Your Excellency, I have come to ask for the body of Jesus."

"What, is he already dead?"

"Yes, Your Excellency."

Pilate looked at him sharply. "Are you one of his followers? You don't look like one."

"Yes, Your Excellency."

Pilate regarded him silently. "Well, I suppose there is no objection." He summoned an officer. "Send a detail of soldiers to take down the prisoners from their crosses."

It was very close to sunset when Joseph finally arrived at Calvary with the little party of soldiers. They would have to work fast. The soldiers pierced Jesus with a lance to make sure that he was dead. Joseph wiped this new wound very gently, and then together they took him down from the cross and carried him to the tomb. They anointed his body with the spices and, wrapping it in the linen cloths, they laid it in the tomb. Then, all pushing together, they rolled the great stone in its groove across the entrance. They would come again, after the Sabbath, but now they must go home. The first horn had already sounded for the Sabbath rest.

Somewhere across the city, in a deep ravine, the body of Judas was lying, dead by his own hand. In the Temple, a group of angry priests argued about how to spend thirty pieces of silver. That morning, Judas had brought back his money.

"I have sinned," he said, "in betraying innocent blood." His face was gray and drawn.

"What is that to us?" they answered sharply. "See to it yourself." He flung down the pieces and fled.

Now they were arguing as to what to do with them. "It is not lawful to put them in the Treasury," they said, "not when they are the price of blood." And so they decided to buy a potter's field as a burial place for strangers. They did not think of it at the time, but they were fulfilling an old prophecy of the prophet Jeremias:

> And they took the thirty pieces of silver,
>   the price of him who was priced,
>   and they gave them for the potter's field.

*   *   *

Early next morning, Pilate was pacing restlessly up and down in his private apartments. He had slept badly and was out of sorts. His wife had been harping on that dream again about Jesus. "See," she said, "there was that earthquake. It bodes no good." But what good would it do to talk about it now? The Nazarene was already dead. Besides, the case was lost from the start. It was the Jewish leaders who had killed him, not he, or Herod either, for that matter. He was not a bad fellow, that Herod, in spite of his reputation! They would have to cling together if ever the people should rise up. He must make friends with Herod — send him some little token of his esteem!

Up and down he walked, up and down. But presently he was interrupted by a servant.

"Your Excellency, you are wanted."

"Who wants me at this hour, fellow?"

"Some of the Jewish leaders, sir."

"Are you lying, fellow? They never come here at this hour on the Sabbath."

"It seems to be a delegation of them, Your Excellency. They seem excited."

"Very well. Show them in."

He seated himself impatiently and waited. He had had enough of these Jewish leaders the day before. He was sick of the whole crowd of them, with their long beards and their nasal voices. He would have to admit the Nazarene was different — and he was dead. That's the way it was in this world! Sitting there, he longed to have the attention of the Emperor for just a moment — just long enough to beg to be transferred to some nice post in Spain or Greece!

When the delegation was ushered in, he turned slowly. "Well," he said testily, "what do you want?"

They stroked their beards and cleared their voices, considering how to begin.

"You remember Jesus of Nazareth, Your Excellency?"

"You don't give me much chance to forget him."

"We should like to guard his tomb. We remember that he made a statement about rising from the dead. We're afraid his followers may steal the body and give out the story that he has risen."

This, thought Pilate, is the most fantastic thing yet!

"Well, guard him then. You have a guard. Go and secure the tomb as you know how." And so a group of thin-faced, scheming Jewish leaders sealed the great stone that closed the tomb of Jesus. A corps of sleepy soldiers took up their watch outside. Somewhere in the lower part of town, eleven frightened disciples of Jesus hid behind closed doors, in terror for their lives. Only one of them had dared to stand by the cross of Jesus. Now they waited, with a group of tear-stained women, for the Sabbath to end. They had no thought of stealing the body of Jesus; they wanted to go to him to pray.

Mary, the mother of Jesus, was praying in the next room — very straight and still. Her eyes were wet, but on her face there was a look of peace. "On the third day," he had said, and now this was the second day. The shadows outside were lengthening. Soon the night would come, and after the night the morning. She had never failed to trust in Jesus, and Jesus had said, "The Son of Man must rise from the dead."

Chapter XXVIII

JESUS RISES ON THE THIRD DAY

ary Magdalen stood in the doorway of the Upper Room, her beautiful eyes swollen with weeping. She looked back once more at the mother of Jesus.

"Are you sure you won't come?"

"No, I will stay here. The blessing of God go with you." Mary's heart was full of compassion for these tear-stained, sorrowing women; but this was *the third day*. It was no use to go to the tomb of Jesus; he would not be there. It was strange that none of his friends seemed to remember about the third day. He had spoken so often about it. But he had let them forget for some purpose, and it was for him to tell them, not for her. He would tell each one in his own way.

Mary Magdalen stood for a moment uncertainly, then she stepped out and went quickly down the stairs. A little group of women was waiting for her outside in the gray light of dawn. Joanna was there, and Mary of Cleophas, and Salome, each carrying something, spices, or precious ointment, or rolls of linen. The burial of Jesus had been hurried because of the Sabbath; they were going back to finish the labor of love.

The streets were almost deserted except for an occasional farmer, bringing his honey or eggs to sell in the market. Now and then a bird twittered or a cock crowed. The women hurried along in silence, each busy with her thoughts. Each had her own private memories of Jesus, her own private grief. For so long they had hung on his words — the precious words they would never forget! It was hard to think they would never hear his voice again.

They came before long to the city gate, but the sleepy sentry did not challenge them. As they started up the slopes of Calvary, suddenly one of them looked up and said, "Who will roll us back the stone?" Who indeed! It was a question they might well have asked, but they were not thinking quite clearly. At any rate, they did not stop, but pressed forward toward the tomb. They tried not to see the three empty crosses, outlined against the sky, but even so, the fresh tears came, the sweet, hot tears of loving sorrow. They headed toward the gate of the garden where the tomb of Jesus was. Perhaps there would be a gardener — someone would surely help them. Their love was too great to stop and think of obstacles.

They hurried their pace almost to a run, the last few yards. Half blinded by their tears, they opened the gate of the garden. Suddenly they stopped short. They were facing the open tomb of Jesus. The stone had already been rolled back.

As they stood startled, they caught sight of one of the guards, stretched on the ground looking as though he were dead. Another lay nearby. They were still breathing, but aside from that, they were as white and motionless as death.

Trembling and silent, the women went slowly toward the empty tomb, seized by a nameless dread. Stooping, they peered into the dark entryway. The tomb was empty.

With a sharp cry, Mary Magdalen turned and started running back toward the gate of the garden, hardly knowing what she did. She stumbled and slackened her pace, but went on in a kind of daze down the slopes of Calvary, never turning around to see whether the others were following.

It was well when she reached the city that no one was yet about, to see this distracted woman with the tear-stained face and disordered clothing, half-walking, half-running through the streets.

A dog started up and barked at her. A small child, straying out of a house, ran back crying.

She did not stop till she reached the house where the Eleven were staying in hiding. She burst into the room without knocking. "They have taken the Lord out of the tomb," she cried. "I know not where they have laid him." She stood in the doorway, gasping for breath, the tears streaming down her face.

Peter and John jumped up and started toward her. *They have taken the Lord? Out of the tomb?* Was Mary Magdalen in her right mind? John had himself helped to roll the great stone in its groove across the doorway of the tomb, and Joseph of Arimathea had brought word about the guards and the seals. How could anyone have taken the body of Jesus? Without waiting to question Mary, they too hurried off through the streets toward the gate of the city. Mary Magdalen, exhausted, started slowly back, the tears still streaming down her face, hardly knowing what she was doing. Soon the two men were out of sight and she was again alone in the streets.

After they passed the gate of the city, they quickened their pace to a run. John, who was young, ran easily, and outdistanced his companion, reaching the tomb first. It was true — the stone was rolled back; but he waited for Peter before going in. After all, it was Peter whom the Master had selected to receive the keys of his kingdom — Peter the Rock. He was a sad, frightened Peter now, but he was still the one whom the Master had chosen. It was right to wait for him.

Peter came up panting, and silently they stooped and entered together, through the low doorway. What Mary Magdalen had said was true, after all. The tomb was indeed empty. But what was more strange, nothing was disturbed. There were no signs anywhere of violence. The linen shroud and bandages were neatly folded. The cloth that had covered the face of Jesus was folded and placed in the corner by itself. No thief would have stopped to do that.

Sad and puzzled, the two men went out again into the gray light of the early morning. The sun was just beginning to touch the tops of the olive trees with light. *They have taken away the Lord and we know not where they have laid him.* Yes, it was true, just as Mary Magdalen had said. But the guards were no longer lying on the ground. They had regained consciousness after the women had left, and picking themselves up, they had made off in fear for their lives. They reported that an earthquake had opened the tomb and that the body of Jesus had been taken. It was a most confused story that they told to the officer on duty in the household of the High Priest. They knew that the sentence of death was hanging over them unless they could prove their point.

Soon messengers were hurrying about through the city. *"The tomb of Jesus is empty. The body of Jesus is nowhere to be found."* All up and down the streets, the message was carried, to the elders, to the chief priests, who had plotted the death of Jesus. Hurrying figures with cloaks drawn close around them came up the street toward Caiphas' house.

"Let us in," they said to the sleepy servant. "The High Priest has sent for us. He wishes to consult the elders and rulers of the people."

And so, once more, they assembled in the great hall of Caiphas' house, with Caiphas and Annas sitting before them.

"What shall we do? Jesus is not where they laid him. His followers will say he has risen from the dead."

"Bribe the soldiers. Make them say the disciples came by night and stole him while they were sleeping."

So, the soldiers were brought in trembling, expecting to hear the worst. Instead, money was put into their shaking hands, bright silver shekels, such as they did not often see. One — two — three — four — five — their eyes bulged with surprise as the coins were counted out. Were they being paid for sleeping at their posts?

"Now look here, you fellows," one of the chief priests said, waving a long finger at them, "if anyone asks you about that empty tomb, you say 'His disciples came by night and stole him while we were sleeping.' And if the governor hears about this, we will persuade him to keep you out of trouble."

It was an absurd story, for if they were sleeping, how could they know who came? But the chief priests were not thinking too clearly at this hour in the morning. As for the soldiers, they went off, caring little for anything except that they were free men with money jingling in their pockets. "*His disciples came by night,*" they rehearsed together, "*and stole him while we were sleeping.*" And so the story spread. It was the easiest money they ever earned.

*   *   *

Peter and John had already left the garden, when Mary Magdalen reached it a second time. The women too were gone, and she leaned against the stone entrance to the tomb and wept. When her tears were somewhat spent, she crouched down and looked into the tomb. She stepped back quickly in wonder and fear, for two men in dazzling white garments sat at the head and foot of the place where Jesus had lain. They looked at her very kindly.

"Woman, why do you weep?" one of them asked.

"Because they have taken away my Lord, and I know not where they have laid him."

Turning around, she saw someone standing behind her. Her eyes were too blurred with tears to see very clearly, but she thought he must be the gardener.

"Sir," she said, "if you have removed him, tell me where you have laid him and I will take him away." Poor, foolish, loving, troubled Mary! How could she have taken him away? But her love knew no bounds that day; it was ready to try the impossible. She turned back again toward the tomb, when the stranger spoke.

"Mary." She turned around quickly. There was only one voice in all the world like that! She fell down on her knees.

"Master!" she said. She could find no other words. Raising her eyes, she looked into the face of Jesus.

He was the same Jesus, loving, gentle, strong.

Fresh tears rushed to her eyes as she looked, but this time they were tears of joy. She looked down again, and there, in front of her, were the feet of Jesus — the feet she had twice bathed and dried with her long, dark hair. But now they were different. They were wounded feet — she could see the wounds between the straps of his sandals. She clasped them in her hot, loving hands.

The voice of Jesus came gently, firmly to her. "Hold me not, for I have not yet ascended to my Father. But go find my brethren and say to them, 'I ascend to my Father and your Father, to my God and your God.'"

She let go of his feet, and suddenly he was gone.

It was a different Mary — a tear-stained but radiant Mary — who rushed up the steps a little later to the Upper Room to share her wonderful news.

"I have seen the Lord," she said excitedly, "and this he said to me: Go and find my brethren and say to them, 'I ascend to my Father and your Father, to my God and your God.'"

But when she had poured out her message, she discovered that she was not the first one to bring back the good news. For the women who had gone with her to the tomb had already come back with a similar story. They too had seen the men in dazzling garments. "Fear not," one of the shining strangers had said, "for I know you seek Jesus who was crucified. He is not here; he is risen. Go quickly and tell his disciples that he is risen from the dead and that he goes before you into Galilee." And so, they had started back, in wonder and joy. They too on the way back had seen Jesus himself — it could not be anyone else. He had said "Hail," in a voice that was the voice of Jesus. "Do not be afraid. Go take word to my brethren that they set out for Galilee. There they shall see me." All this the women had reported. The disciples looked at one another, and then back at Mary Magdalen and the other women. Could they believe these reports? Or were they only the imaginings of hysterical women, upset by all their grief? They would wait till Peter and John got back. They could be trusted to be accurate witnesses.

A little later John climbed the stairs with a strangely moved and shaken Peter. "I have seen Jesus," Peter said; that was all he reported. But they could see he was again at peace. Poor Peter had so much to reproach himself for! "To think that I denied him!"

he had said over and over in these past troubled hours. "To think that I was not with him when he died!" But now he was at peace — for he had seen Jesus. What Jesus said to him was a secret, but once again he was Peter the Rock.

And yet, even after Peter and John came back, hope and doubt struggled in the minds of the disciples. They did not dare to hope too much. It would be too terrible to be deceived.

Chapter XXIX

JESUS RETURNS TO THE
UPPER ROOM

HE big, sprawling city of Jeru-
salem was full of bustling life on the first day after the Great
Sabbath. Pilgrims who had come for the Passover remained to
celebrate. They gathered in the market place to talk, and over
and over the talk turned to Jesus.

"Yes, sir, they say the body of Jesus was stolen. You know —
Jesus the Nazarene. They say he called himself the king of the
Jews. He was killed, you know, on the eve of the Feast. They say
his body was stolen from the tomb."

"Stolen?"

"Yes, sir. Stolen by his disciples — that's what the soldiers say.
The chief priests are very angry. They thought they had heard
the last of him."

"What's that, Lady? You wonder about the Man Jesus? You say
he healed your servant? You'd better not let any of the Jews
hear you speak well of him, lady. You'd better keep still if you
know any good about Jesus." And so the talk ran on.

But not all of the pilgrims stayed over, especially the poorer

199

ones, or those who lived quite near and could visit the city often. That was the way with Cleophas and his friend. He wasn't any relation of Mary of Cleophas. He and his friend were farmers living near Emmaus, and they were anxious to get back to their lands, for the crops needed them. Besides, this Passover had not been like other feasts. It had been a sad, agonizing Passover, for they were disciples of Jesus. They were in no mood to celebrate.

"What do you think about that story of the women?" one of them was saying as they hurried along the dusty road. "Do you think Jesus really could have risen, as they said?"

"They were all hysterical, every one of them. You couldn't be sure of anything they'd say. They'd believe what they wanted to believe. Now if Peter or John had come back and told us he had seen Jesus, it would be different. And yet Peter is hardly himself yet. Poor Peter! He'll never forget he denied the Lord!"

"Did you think it would end like this? Of course, the Master did speak sometimes about carrying one's cross, but he spoke so often in figures that you couldn't be sure when to take him literally and when not. Did you think when he entered Jerusalem with everyone waving the palm branches that they would turn so quickly against him? I thought maybe this time he really would be made king. The people had spoken about it so often, and after he raised up Lazarus, more and more seemed to be flocking to him."

"You don't get to the city as often as I. There were a lot of people against him, almost from the start. But still, I had hoped. . . . Yes, I had hoped. . . ."

They had slackened their pace as they talked, and presently they were aware of someone behind them.

"Yes, I had hoped too. It was all a wonderful dream — but it is over. It is hard to believe he will never come walking over these roads any more, with the Twelve following him, and the children and the sick crowding around for his blessing. It was a wonderful dream, but now we must put it behind us and get back to our crops."

The steps behind them were coming closer. They paused a moment and the traveler overtook them. It was good to have a companion on the road.

"Good day to you, stranger."

"Good day, friends."

The traveler walked along beside them, suiting his pace to theirs. He was silent a moment, and then he asked, in a voice that was faintly familiar, "What words are these you are exchanging as you walk and are sad?"

How much had he heard? They did not know; but his manner was friendly. They could not believe he would wish them any harm.

"How is it you don't know?" Cleophas answered. "Are you a stranger in Jerusalem that you don't know the things that have happened in these days?"

"What things, friend?" asked the stranger.

"About Jesus of Nazareth, whom they crucified. We had hoped great things of him."

He looked toward the stranger. Was it safe to go on? The man appeared kind and sympathetic. "He was mighty in word and work, and we were hoping it was he who should redeem Israel." He went on and told how the chief priests and rulers had delivered him up to be crucified. Then he hesitated. Would it be safe to go on and tell everything? He longed to empty out his heart, and he had never found a more understanding listener. As he hesitated, the stranger looked at him so kindly that he decided to tell all.

"And what is more, certain women of our company, who were at the tomb before it was light, astounded us, for not finding his body, they came saying that they had also seen a vision of angels who said he is alive. Some of our company went and found it, just as the women said, but they did not see him."

He paused, and the stranger began to speak, kindly, quietly, quickening his pace a little. It was strange, but they had not yet had a good look at him; he kept either a little behind or a little ahead, and his face was partly hidden by his cloak.

"Oh foolish and slow of heart to believe in all that the prophets have spoken," he said, gently but kindly. "Did not the Christ have to suffer these things before entering into his glory?" Then, beginning with Moses and all the prophets, he interpreted what the Scriptures had said about the Messias. Was it not always prophesied that he would suffer? Was he not to be a "Man of Sorrows," a "worm and no man"? Every year the Jews sacrificed thousands of lambs in the great marble Temple at Jerusalem to show their need of God, their love of God, their sorrow for their sins. But was not the Messias to be the "Lamb of God," and must he not be sacrificed too to save men from their sins? Was not this all a part of God's plan?

Little by little, they began to understand that the cross was not a mistake. It was not a failure. It was a sign of God's love.

Their hearts began to burn within them. They could listen to this man forever. "Stay with us," they pleaded when they reached Emmaus and he prepared to leave them. "The day is growing late." He smiled graciously and turned down the dusty lane with them. He was wonderfully kind and friendly, this stranger. He talked with them till the evening meal was spread and then he sat down to table with them. It was then that he did the thing that made them know him. He took bread and broke it and blessed it and gave it to them. Suddenly, they knew he was Jesus. They knew him in the breaking of the bread.

They took the bread with trembling hands, shut their eyes to give thanks to God, and ate it. When they looked up again, Jesus was gone.

For a moment they sat speechless. Then Cleophas said, "We must go back and tell the Eleven." Scarcely stopping to eat, they hurried out and started back over the way they had come.

"What has got into them," the wife of Cleophas thought as she put away the cheese, the wine, the figs. But she noticed that the bread had been eaten. "At least they have had that," she thought with satisfaction.

*   *   *

The friends of Jesus sat crowded together in the Upper Room, talking excitedly. It had been a strange day, this first day after the Great Sabbath, and they still did not know what to think. All but one of the Eleven was there — Thomas the Twin. The women were there and some of the other disciples. Matthias was there, and Barsabas. They seemed almost like the Eleven. It was dark outside now and the lamps were lit. The doors and windows were barred, for the tale the soldiers had spread about stealing the body of Jesus made them fearful.

The women had set out supper, but no one had eaten much — only a little honey, a bite or two of fish. Now they had cleared it away.

"Of course, they saw something," one of the Eleven was saying. "The women couldn't all have been mistaken, and Peter too. But sometimes people see spirits."

"Yes, but the Magdalen touched him. She felt his feet with her hands."

They had been arguing back and forth like this all day, drawn between hope and doubt. They wanted to believe, but they feared to believe — afraid lest they be deceived.

Suddenly, as they were talking of these things, they heard a voice saying, "Peace be to you. It is I — do not be afraid." There, in the midst of them, stood Jesus. The door had not been opened — it was still tightly barred. Then this could not be really Jesus; it must be a spirit after all! The group broke up into panic.

"Why are you disturbed?" he said gently. Surely that voice was the voice of Jesus. "Why do doubts arise in your hearts? See my hands and feet, that it is I myself. Feel me and see, for a spirit does not have flesh and bones, as you see I have." He showed his hands and feet, with the prints of the nails still in them. He even showed them his side, with the wound from the lance. He was as gentle with them as though they were frightened children.

But still, some of them were afraid. Then he said, just like the old Jesus, "Have you anything to eat?" Surely, if he ate before them, they would believe, for no one ever heard of a spirit eating!

"We have fish and a little honeycomb," they said, and they

brought these out and set them before him on the table. He ate in front of them, and passed what was left to them to eat. Then, as he sat with them at table, he rebuked them very gently for their unbelief.

When they had all eaten, he rose and looked around at their upturned faces. Just so, he had stood, on the night of the Last Supper, before he was betrayed. "Peace be to you," he said. There was something both gentle and solemn in his manner. He looked around at those of the Eleven who were present — which was all except Thomas. He seemed to be missing Thomas, but he did not ask about him. He was going to do something very important; Thomas would not be present when he did it. But he would see Thomas later. He would not make the other ten wait.

Raising his hand, he said very solemnly: "As the Father has sent me, I also send you." He breathed on them, and then he went on: "Receive the Holy Spirit. Whose sins you shall forgive, they are forgiven; and whose sins you shall retain they are retained."

The ten disciples stood in breathless silence. At the Last Supper, after he had turned the bread into his body and the wine into his blood, he had said to them, "Do this in remembrance of me." Now he had given them the power to forgive sins in his name. First they had been his disciples; then he had called them his friends. Now, little by little, he was making them his priests.

They prayed for a moment, in awe and wonder. When they looked up again, Jesus was gone. They stood silently, looking at one another. What did they mean, those words that he had spoken? What was he asking of them? Was he always going to be coming and going like this, remaining only a few minutes at a time?

Their minds were full of questions, but in their hearts there was nothing but joy. They were no longer afraid or in doubt. Jesus, who was crucified, had risen as he said. This was the greatest miracle of all.

They were quiet after he left, hushed by the wonder of his words.

They were still sitting thoughtfully around the table, some time later, when there came a knock at the door.

One of them rose to answer it. "Who is there?"

"It is I — Cleophas. We are back from Emmaus."

Back from Emmaus — at this time of night! That was strange. The door was unbarred and opened, and Cleophas and his companion came in.

"We have seen the Lord!" Cleophas exclaimed.

"And so have we!" the disciples replied. And so they exchanged experiences. "We knew him in the breaking of the bread," Cleophas said. "But all along the way, he had taught us the most wonderful things. It was strange we did not know him." It was one of the strange things of this very strange day. Now all of them had seen Jesus except Thomas, and perhaps he had seen him too. Perhaps the Master had appeared to Thomas, as he had appeared that morning to Peter. He seemed to be showing himself to each one.

The lamps were burning low, that evening, when there was a second knock at the door of the Upper Room and Thomas came in.

"Thomas," they cried out excitedly, "you should have been here! The Master was here and ate with us." They went on to tell him what had happened.

"And we saw him too at Emmaus," Cleophas added. "We knew him in the breaking of the bread."

Thomas stood looking from one to another. He was skeptical by nature, and he had heard enough unbelievable tales for one day. And perhaps he was just a little irritated at being away when so much was going on. At any rate he shook his head and said: "Unless I see in his hands the print of the nails and put my finger into the place of the nails, and put my hand into his side, I will not believe."

The other ten gasped a little. Who was Thomas to set down conditions like this? But the Master understood Thomas and he was very forgiving. Besides, they had to admit that they too had been slow to believe.

The week that followed was a strange, tense week. They kept waiting for Jesus to come again, but each night when they met, no one could report having seen him.

"Perhaps we should go back to our homes," some of them said.

"He said to meet him in Galilee. Perhaps he is waiting for us there."

"Wait another day, then we will go," they decided each evening.

Finally, a week after his first visit, he came again. Just as before, the doors were all barred, and they were seated together in the Upper Room, but this time Thomas was with them.

Suddenly they heard again the familiar words: "Peace be to you," and looking up, they saw Jesus in their midst.

He turned immediately to Thomas. "Bring here your finger," he said, "and see my hands, and bring here your hand, and put it in my side, and be not unbelieving, but believing."

Thomas drew back. What had he done to challenge the Master like this? The Master who was the Lord, who was — yes, even God! He fell upon his knees before Jesus.

"My Lord and my God," he exclaimed, full of wonder and grief. It was the greatest act of faith that any of the Eleven had made.

Jesus turned his loving eyes on Thomas. He was well content with this proof of his disciple's loving repentance. But with just a shade of reproof, he added, "Because you have seen me, you have believed. Blessed are they who have not seen, and yet have believed."

Suddenly he was gone. None of them ever afterward doubted that Jesus was truly risen from the dead.

Chapter XXX

JESUS COMMISSIONS HIS DISCIPLES
AS APOSTLES

ETER rested back against the oars and watched the first streaks of light moving across the sky. The dark water slapped softly against the sides of the boat. What was the use of trying any longer? They had been fishing all night and had caught nothing.

Peter fingered the splintery handles of the oars. It was nearly three years since he had followed his trade of fishing with any regularity. Instead, he had been a "fisher of men," going up and down through Galilee and Judea with Jesus and the Twelve. But now those days were over, and their plans were completely unsettled. It was true that the Master had said to them in Jerusalem, "As the Father sent me, I also send you," but they did not know quite what he meant by it. They had seen him only once since then — the night he had shown himself to Thomas. They had come to Galilee, in obedience to his instructions to the women, but he had not yet appeared to them. And so, that evening, Peter had said, "I am going fishing."

Anything definite looked good to them, after their uncertainty, and so the others answered, "We will go too." There were seven of them all together. They were glad to feel the boat beneath them, the fresh breeze in their faces, the oars in their hands. It had been strange to be back in Galilee without Jesus. People did not know quite what to say to them. "Those are the disciples of Jesus," they could hear people saying in the market place. "Poor fellows, they pinned their hopes on the wrong cause that time!" The Eleven could not very well reply, "He is not dead; he is risen," for no one would believe them — not until he had shown himself in Galilee.

At first they had not minded that they were catching no fish. They were enjoying the mild night air and the old, familiar exercise. But when hour after hour passed without success, that fact just heightened their general restlessness. And so Peter, fingering his oars, was thinking: What is the use of trying longer?

"Let's take in the nets," he said, and the others started pulling. It was easy to do with empty nets!

Suddenly they heard someone calling from the shore.

"Young men, have you any fish?" That was strange, so early in the morning, on this rather deserted stretch of beach!

Looking up, Peter could dimly make out, in the early morning light, a man standing on the shore looking out at them.

"No!" he shouted back, rather ruefully.

"Cast the net to the right of the boat and you will find them," the stranger called back.

Peter, willing to try anything as a show of courtesy toward a stranger, motioned to the others to do as the man had said. They took an empty net from the boat and sent it swinging into the dark water. There was a quick splash, a widening circle of ripples, and then suddenly the ropes tightened. The net began to sag. Almost before they knew what had happened, it was full to bursting with fish. Excitedly the men sprang to the ropes and started pulling. But John, who was next to Peter, leaned toward him and said, "It is the Lord."

Peter's mind, too, was stirring with memories of another morning, nearly three years before, when almost the same thing had happened. It had been on the day when Jesus said, *I will make you fishers of* men. Of course John was right; of course it was the Lord.

The boat was not very far from shore, and the water was shallow. Gathering his tunic about him, Peter stepped over the side of the boat and made quickly toward the shore. He was still the same impulsive, loving Peter! The others came after him with the boat, dragging the bursting net. Later, after Jesus had gone, they laid the fish out in shining, silver rows on the sand and counted them. There were a hundred and fifty-three — and the net was not even torn! That in itself was a miracle.

When Peter reached the shore, he found Jesus leaning over a small fire, broiling a fish. Near by was a loaf of bread. "Bring here some of the fishes that you caught just now," Jesus said, and he motioned to them to come and eat.

The men came rather shyly, for they were more in awe of this new, risen Jesus than of the Jesus they had known before. Yet he could not have been kinder. Sitting down around the glowing coals where the fish lay broiling, they did not dare to ask, "Who are you?" but they all knew in their hearts it was the Lord.

Jesus took the bread and broke it and gave it to them, and then the fish. And so they sat there, eating, while the early morning sun climbed slowly above the hills. It was like many mornings they had spent with Jesus — and yet it was very different; it was still more wonderful. For all the time they were thinking: This is Jesus, *risen from the dead.*

When they had finished and had risen to their feet, Jesus turned to Peter and said: "Simon, son of John, do you love me more than these do?"

The blood surged quickly into Peter's honest face. What could he say — he who had three times denied his Lord on the night when he needed him most? Could he dare to say to Jesus he loved him more than any of the others? Could he say he loved Jesus more than John loved him — John who had stayed all through his three hours on the cross?

For a moment he was silent; then he answered with a quickly-beating heart, "Yes, Lord, you know that I love you."

"Feed my lambs," said Jesus quietly.

A minute later, Jesus spoke again. "Simon, son of John, do you love me?"

Peter was troubled. Why did the Master ask him again? Did he not believe him? "Yes, Lord," he answered a second time, "you know that I love you."

"Feed my lambs," Jesus answered again, still in the same quiet voice.

After another minute of silence, Jesus said a third time: "Simon, son of John, do you love me?"

Now Peter was really grieved. The others were standing about awkwardly, wondering what Jesus had in his mind.

"Lord, you know all things," said Peter humbly. "You know that I love you."

"Feed my sheep," said Jesus.

Peter had fulfilled his penance. He was ready now to receive his burden — the burden of the infant Church — a burden which he would carry gloriously, even to the death of the cross.

Jesus looked at him very lovingly. "Amen, I say to you, when you were young you girded yourself and walked where you willed, but when you are old, you will stretch out your hands and another will guide you, and will lead you where you do not will." He was speaking of the death Peter would die for Jesus. After a moment of silence, he added. "Follow me."

Jesus turned and started off down the beach. Peter hurried to follow him. Close behind Peter came John.

"Lord," asked Peter, "what of this man?" indicating John. But Jesus was not ready yet to answer that question. "If I wish him to remain till I come, what is that to you? Follow me."

Some of the other disciples, hearing, thought Jesus had said, "John is not to die," and so a strange rumor began to grow about him. But John himself always insisted, "He did not say 'He is not to die,' but rather, 'If I wish him to remain until I come, what is that to you?' " It was a way Jesus had of silencing a question.

They walked along the shore, Jesus and the disciples, in the early

morning, in this new companionship that was so wonderful. Jesus
did not say much more to them that morning. But before he left
them, he told them of the time and place for another meeting —
on a certain mountain they knew very well. Jesus loved mountains,
and so too did the Eleven. His dearest meetings with them had
been on mountains. They would be there even earlier than he
said, waiting for him to come.

*   *   *

The disciples of Jesus climbed the steep trail in silence on
the appointed day — Peter first, then John, then the rest of the
Eleven. They quite naturally grouped themselves in that order.
There was no sound but the noise of their sandals on the rocky
path and the occasional twitter of a bird. The sun was warm on
their backs, but not yet hot, and the air was sweet with flowering
trees. It was a lovely day to be climbing a mountain. Far below
them lay the lake, blue and glittering, with its white specks of
sails, and the fields looked like green velvet. But the Eleven were
not thinking of the view as they climbed the rough trail. They
were thinking only of Jesus.

They had seen him more than once since that day by the shore
of the lake when he fed them the bread and fish. Once he had
even appeared before more than five thousand people. The crowd
had gone away marveling. "Surely, this is Jesus," they had exclaimed.
"It is Jesus, risen from the dead!" Now every village in Galilee
was buzzing with the news. "Were you there that day?" people
asked each other. "Did you see Jesus? Was it really he?" Those who
saw him believed, but others were uncertain. Who ever heard of
rising from the dead!

The Eleven were glad that he had showed himself to so many.
It would make their task easier, for it was hard to make people
believe when they had not seen. If even Thomas had doubted,
what could they expect of these others? It was almost a miracle
when men did believe. They could hear Jesus saying to Thomas,
"Blessed are they who have not seen, and yet have believed."

They were thinking of these things as they climbed the mountain that morning. When they reached the top, they stood catching their breath, and looking out over the wide expanse before them. They were earlier than Jesus had said; they would have some time to wait.

But Jesus did not wait for the appointed hour. Suddenly, with no warning, he stood among them. They would never grow accustomed to the miracle of it! First he was not there, and then, the next minute, he was with them, standing quietly among them, as though there was nothing strange about it at all. But today he seemed even more wonderful. With one accord they fell down on their knees and worshiped him. As Thomas had said that night in Jerusalem, truly he was their Lord and their God.

He drew near to them and started speaking very earnestly. On the night of the Last Supper he had given them the wonderful power of turning bread and wine into his body and blood. But that was not all they were to do in his name. "All power in heaven and on earth has been given to me," he said. "Go, therefore, and teach all nations, baptizing in the name of the Father and of the Son and of the Holy Spirit, teaching them to observe all that I have commanded you; and behold, I am with you all days, even unto the consummation of the world."

In a moment, he was gone.

The little group of eleven stood alone on the top of the mountain, trying to grasp the meaning of his words to them. He did not want them to go back to their old trades, to their boats and their nets. The old invitation still held, that he had given them three years before on the shore of the lake: "Come follow me, and I will make you fishers of men." That's what he meant when he said, "Go and teach all nations." But that was a wider field than they had ever dreamed of. "Teaching all nations" meant more than just Galilee and Judea; it meant Greece and Rome and Spain. They gasped as they thought what it meant.

And it was something new to baptize "in the name of the Father and of the Son and of the Holy Ghost." That was the baptism of Christ; it was different from the baptism of John.

But most wonderful of all was his promise: "I will be with you all days" he had said, *even to the end of the world.*

They stood on their mountaintop, looking out beyond the green fields of Galilee, beyond the Lake of Genesareth with its white sails, into the great future that lay before them. Then silently, soberly, they turned and started down the mountain. They were no longer merely disciples, they were apostles; *they were men whom the Master had sent.*

Chapter XXXI

JESUS ASCENDS INTO HEAVEN AND SENDS IN HIS PLACE THE HOLY SPIRIT

JESUS did not mean his eleven disciples to begin their work in Galilee; he meant them to begin it in Jerusalem. And so it was that ten days before the Feast of Pentecost they were gathered once more in the Upper Room with Jesus in their midst. It was wonderful to have him with them in the old familiar way and to know that the cross was behind him, with nothing more to fear. It was still more wonderful to begin to see him as he really was — God as well as Man, one God with the Father and the Holy Spirit. They only dimly understood this yet. "When the Holy Spirit comes upon you," Jesus kept promising, "then you shall know all truth." But what they already knew was wonderful.

It was only forty days since the Last Supper, when he had washed their feet and had given them the wonderful bread that was his body. They had been heavy of heart that night, with a heaviness they could not understand. He was going away from them then, and they did not know where. He kept trying to tell them about the cross, but they could not seem to follow his meaning.

Now again he was going away, and they did not even want to ask where. They knew he was going to the Father, and they were glad for his sake. One or two still hoped that before he went, he would establish an earthly kingdom. They hoped he would show himself to all men, as the prophets had described him, sitting on the throne of David. They still could not quite understand that his kingdom was "not of this world," but a kingdom inside men's souls. But not even this troubled them, for he had given them his peace.

Once again he went over the things he had been telling them for forty days. It was right that Christ should suffer and rise again from the dead on the third day. The cross was all a part of God's plan. They must preach repentance to all nations, beginning from Jerusalem. They must speak with the authority of witnesses, for they had seen these things with their own eyes. They did not have to do these things alone; the Holy Spirit would help them. "I send forth upon you the promise of the Father."

He looked at each one in turn very lovingly. They had had to learn hard lessons in these past three years. They had had to get rid of rashness and obstinacy and fear; and they had had to learn trust and humility and love. Now all they needed was the Holy Spirit to strengthen and guide them — but without that they could do nothing.

"John, indeed, baptized with water," he said to them, "but you shall be baptized with the Holy Spirit not many days hence. Wait here in the city until you are clothed with power from on high. You shall receive power when the Holy Spirit comes upon you, and you shall be witnesses for me in Jerusalem, and in all Judea and Samaria, and even to the very ends of the earth."

As they sat in the Upper Room listening to him, they did not know how soon he would be leaving them. They did not know this was the last time he would be with them, speaking to them in his quiet, loving way. But when he had finished speaking, he rose and led them down into the street. He led them through the streets and out the city gate to the Bethany road. There were not many people about as they hurried along. Those whom they met paid little attention to the small group of Galilean fishermen hurrying out of the city. They would not have guessed that something very strange was about to happen.

Jesus led them up the Bethany road to the top of the Mount of Olives. He stopped at a spot which he loved. On the one side lay the city of Jerusalem, shimmering with light; on the other the road zigzagged down the hillside between fields and olive orchards. It was here that Jesus had wept over Jerusalem and had been met by the crowds singing *Hosanna to the Son of David.*

Gathering the Eleven about him, he lifted up his hands and blessed them. They stood grouped expectantly around him, waiting for him to speak. But he did not speak. Instead, he was lifted up very slowly before their eyes. They watched him with wonder and awe, rising up higher and higher toward heaven until a cloud took him out of their sight. While they were gazing up to heaven, still staring at the spot where they had last seen him, two men in shining white garments appeared beside them.

"Men of Galilee, why do you stand looking up to heaven?" they asked. "This Jesus who has been taken up from you into heaven will come in the same way as you have seen him going up to heaven."

The Eleven stood speechless with wonder, but before they could answer, the angels had disappeared. They were standing alone at the top of the Mount of Olives, with the city shining below them on one side, and the road zigzagging down on the other.

No one said a word for some time. Then Peter turned and started back down the way they had come. The others followed after him in silence. They would go back to the Upper Room and pray. Jesus had said, "Wait here in the city until you are clothed with power from on high." He had said it would come "not many days hence." That was all they needed to know.

*   *   *

The Feast of Pentecost dawned fair and bright. No cloud darkened the sky. No wind ruffled the banners of the great Caesar that fluttered above the gates of the praetorium. Sun glittered from the gilded turrets of the Temple as the crowds thronged the broad esplanade, coming to make their offering of the *Loaves*. For the wheat that had just unfurled at the time of the Passover had ripened and been harvested. The first flour of the harvest had been baked into bread as an offering to the Lord of the Harvest. It was for this that the great Feast of Pentecost had been created — the Feast of the First Fruits.

Pilgrims came from farther away for the Feast of Pentecost than for any of the other great feasts. It was a better time of year to travel, and there were fewer duties to keep men at home. Pilgrims came from beyond Palestine, from Egypt, from Greece, from Rome, even from Persia and Arabia, men who were Jews in religion, but not in language and dress.

They crowded into Jerusalem in rich Oriental robes and turbans, in Roman togas and high laced sandals. They stood in foreign-looking groups, talking their strange foreign languages; but when they entered the great silver and bronze gates of the Temple, they were at home. It was good to peer through into the Holy Place, where the fires smoldered all day in praise of the one God; for they came from lands where men worshiped strange, pagan gods and offered incense to idols. Yes, to come to Jerusalem was a kind of homecoming, though they might never have been there before.

While the crowds were growing each day in the streets outside, the friends of Jesus stayed quietly together indoors, praying. Mary, the mother of Jesus, was the center of the little group, counseling them, encouraging them, and making them think of Jesus in a hundred small ways. She had his same kindness, his gentleness, his calmness, and she looked at them out of eyes that were very like his eyes. She cared for the same things too — for the poor, the sick, the old, for sinners who needed to be brought back to God, for the good who were weary and needed strength.

If Mary was the heart of the little group, Peter was its head, because Jesus had willed it to be so. Even Mary always said, when any questions came up, "Ask Peter." Then he would pray, and give the best answer he could, but it was hard when he had not yet received "the power from on high." It would become easier after that.

They spent much time in the Upper Room, they and all the other friends of Jesus. But they no longer barred the doors and windows for fear of the chief priests and Pharisees. They went daily to the Temple to pray and praise God, but no place seemed to bring God so close as the Upper Room. Perhaps they were already vaguely realizing that when Jesus had broken the bread and lifted up the cup, and said, "This is my body," "This is my blood," he had begun a new kind of worship. He had been starting a new kind of sacrifice, more pleasing to God than the sacrifice of lambs and doves in the Temple. They would see all this more clearly when the Holy Spirit had come.

It was not surprising, therefore, that on the morning of Pentecost, the friends of Jesus were gathered in the Upper Room. Mary was there, with the other women near her, and Peter, with the rest of the Twelve. There had been Twelve again for nearly a week, for Matthias had been chosen by lot to take the place of Judas. Many of the other friends of Jesus were present too, so that the Upper Room was crowded to the door. It was early in the morning and all was very still.

They all sat silently, praying. *Come, Holy Spirit*, they were praying in their hearts. *Come and visit us with power from on high, so that we may do the work of Jesus*. They knew Jesus would keep his promise, but he liked them to pray for what they needed. *Seek and you shall find*, he had said to them. And so they were praying, over and over, *Come, Holy Spirit*. . . .

Suddenly they heard a strange noise. It came down through the house like a very great wind. It filled the whole house with its din like a violent tempest, but the house did not shake, the way it would have done with a tempest. People looked at each other in surprise, and as they did so, they saw long streamers of light, like tongues of fire, coming down and resting on each one. But most wonderful of all was the joy that poured into their hearts, a joy that was peaceful and strong, like the joy they used to feel with

Jesus. It was the joy that only comes to those who are on fire with the love of God.

They looked at each other in wonder and awe, and then they looked at Mary. She was smiling as though she knew a secret. Was this the wonderful new baptism that Jesus had spoken of? Was this the Holy Spirit coming into their hearts? Surely, it must be that.

Scarcely knowing what they did, they rushed out of the room and down the narrow stairs into the street. There were crowds outside in the street, shouting and pointing. For all over that part of the city people had heard the strange sound and had seen the tongues of fire.

But the sounds had ceased now, and the tongues of flame had vanished and the house looked very ordinary. "What was it?" people asked each other. "Did you hear that sound? Can you tell us what happened?"

The disciples of Jesus, coming from the house, mingled with the crowd, praising God. They still scarcely knew what they were saying. Suddenly the people around them began to stand still and listen. For they came from many foreign lands, but each one heard the disciples of Jesus praising God in his own language. The Egyptians heard them in their tongue, and the Greeks in theirs, and the Romans in theirs, and the Arabians in theirs. Yet were not these people who spoke all Galileans? And humble ones, too, judging by their clothes!

"How is it," they asked each other, "that each of us hears them speak in our own language?" Most of them were very full of wonder; but a few of them scoffed. "Can't you see? They are drunk with new wine!" It was a foolish answer, indeed!

Peter knew by the Holy Spirit within him that the moment had come at last for the little group to begin their mission. Right here in front of the house, they would begin to teach all nations! He stepped forward and started to speak. "This Jesus whom you crucified," he said loudly and boldly, "has risen from the dead!" and no one dared to scoff at him, though it was a strange statement to their ears. He stood there on the morning of Pentecost, preaching the message of Jesus to a silent, awe-struck crowd. He did not speak like an awkward, untaught fisherman; he spoke like the Vicar of Christ. That day three thousand of his hearers believed and were baptized. The Church of Christ had begun its long, slow mission, which would not end until the end of time.

Go and teach all nations . . . and lo, I will be with you all days . . . even till the end of the world. . . .

Epilogue

THE APOSTLE JOHN BEGINS TO WRITE HIS GOSPEL

JOHN, the "beloved disciple," sat with his writing tablet on his knees, thinking. He was an old man now, very old. He was so old, in fact, that the young men carried him to the secret meeting place of the Christians to celebrate the Holy Mysteries. Yet it was wonderful how steady his wrinkled old hands were, with their thin blue veins, when he raised up the holy bread and said in his tired old voice:

> Take and eat ye all of this,
> for this is my body. . . .

He could never say those words and know that the Lord lay clasped in his weak hands without the tears coming to his eyes. Often they streamed down his face so that it was impossible to hide them. "See how he loves the Lord," the Christians would say to one another.

"You must write," men had urged him often in these last years. "You must write about Jesus while there is yet time. There must be much you have never told, and you are the last one who knew him. You must write for us and those who come after us — our children and our children's children."

Yes, there was much that he had never told, much that he never could tell. The world itself could not contain all the books that would have to be written to tell all there was about Jesus. But he was too old to write. All he could say when people asked him to speak to them was, "Little children, love one another." When they replied a little impatiently, "You have told us that before," he would say, "That is all that matters. Little children, love one another." Then his thoughts would slip back into the past, to the time when he had heard Jesus first say those words.

Yet if God wanted him to write about Jesus, God would tell him what to say. "I will write," he finally consented, "but you must ask the whole Church to fast, to beg God's help." He had asked them to read to him, too. He must hear what had already been written about Jesus so that he would know what to say. There was Matthew's account, the first — written especially for the Jews. It answered all their difficulties and objections. Matthew had not sat year after year collecting taxes without getting to know his own people. And there was Mark's account, written in Rome for the Christians there, with the help of Peter. And there was Luke's, with its lovely stories about the birth of Jesus which he had learned from our Lady. Luke was a physician and an artist, and both doctors and artists notice details which others miss. And of course there were letters, many letters, especially those of Peter and Paul. Paul's letters to the Corinthians searched deep into the secrets of God's love.

"I don't need to say what they have said," thought John to himself, as he sat with his writing tablet on his knees. Some things, yes — the big important things. You could not leave those out and have it still the story of Jesus. But he must think chiefly of what no one else had mentioned.

The tired old mind went back over the years, past the travels and persecutions, past the early years when he had lived with our Lady and the little Church was just beginning to reach out from Jerusalem. It had been wonderful to live with her. She was very like Jesus, mothering, as she did, the whole Church. When she died they had wept, yet they could not help being glad that she had been taken up to be with Jesus.

It was hard to realize that Peter was dead, crucified head down in Rome; that Paul was dead, beheaded on the Appian Way. Paul was so much a part of the Church that it was hard to remember he had once persecuted it. They were all gone now, the Twelve all gone, the Seventy all gone — gone by the sword, gone by the fire, gone by the beasts in the arena. All were gone to Jesus, slain for the sake of Jesus. Yes, the Christians were right. He was the only one left; he should set down what he could.

He could remember the very first time he had ever seen Jesus. "It was at the ninth hour," he mused. Shutting his eyes, he could see the Master walking with John the Baptist down by the Jordan. He could remember each thing that happened at the marriage feast of Cana. He must include that, for the others had not written of it — they had not been there.

Most of all he remembered the Last Supper, on the night when Jesus was betrayed. He remembered the wonderful words of Jesus, about the vine and the branches, about abiding in his love and all being one and loving one another. No one else had written of these either. And he must fill in more details about the trial and death of Jesus, for he was the only one who had been there all the way through. The memories came crowding as he sat with his writing tablet. But the old hands lay still. He was not ready yet to write. He had more thinking to do first.

There was something more to tell about Jesus than just what he said and did. He must try to tell more of who he was. That was what really mattered, and yet it was hard to put into words so that others would understand. He sat there thinking about words, about how poor they were, how little one could say with them. There was only one word that mattered — *Jesus*. Jesus was the Word of God. He liked that thought. He let his mind rest in it a while. Then he stirred himself and looked down at the tablet on his knees.

The time had come to start writing, but how should he begin? Mark had started with the preaching of John the Baptist. Luke had gone back to the message of the angel Gabriel to Mary. Matthew, who was interested in Jewish history, had traced back the human ancestry of Jesus to David. But he, John, must go farther back than any of them. He must go back before David, before Moses, before Noah and the flood. He must go back even before Adam and Eve, though it was to them God first promised the Redeemer, after the first sin. He must go back before there was any world, back to God when there was nothing but God. That was where he must begin about Jesus — Jesus, the Word of God, Jesus who, with the Father and the Holy Spirit, was God!

John sat with his eyes closed, looking back to the beginning of time. And then he looked ahead to the end of time, when Jesus would come to judge the world. He sat very still with the bright visions hurrying through his mind — the visions that were almost impossible to put into words. At last he picked up his stylus to write. His hand and mind were steady now, very steady for so old a man. The whole Church had been praying for him, fasting and praying, and the Spirit of God had taken hold of him. He leaned forward over the tablet, and with strong clear strokes he began to write:

> In the beginning was the Word,
> and the Word was with God,
> and the Word was God. . . .